SECOND EDITION Applying Mathematics

Raye A. Carlaw
Specialist — Special Education
Belleville, Ontario

Paul T. Raithby
Specialist in Special Education
Maplewood Vocational School
Scarborough, Ontario

McGRAW-HILL RYERSON LIMITED

Toronto Montreal New York St. Louis San Francisco Auckland Bogotá Guatemala Hamburg Lisbon
London Madrid Mexico New Delhi Panama Paris San Juan São Paulo Singapore Sidney Tokyo

Applying Mathematics 2nd edition

Canadian Cataloguing in Publication Data

Carlaw, Raye A., date
  Applying mathematics

ISBN 0-07-077886-8

1. Arithmetic - 1961-   I. Raithby, Paul T.
II. Title.

QA107.C37 1981   513   C81-095073-1

    4 5 6 7 8 9 0 9 8

Printed and bound in Canada

CONTENTS

CHAPTER ONE
WHOLE NUMBERS

Addition

✓ **Addition facts to 10:**

1	3	5	7	9	2	1	5	6	2	1	5
0	2	4	2	0	4	6	2	3	7	9	3

4	2	1	2	6	8	1	2	4	5	2	9
6	8	2	6	4	1	7	0	4	5	2	1

3	5	1	7	4	1	1	6	3	7	3	1
5	0	4	0	2	5	8	0	4	3	0	2

6	4	1	2	6	4	3	2	4	2	5	4
1	3	1	3	2	5	1	5	0	1	1	1

3	3	3	4	8
3	7	6	6	2

Addition facts 11 to 18:

9	7	8	6	8	9	5	6	4	7	9	9
2	4	5	6	7	8	9	7	8	8	3	9

9	6	9	5	8	7	8	7	3	4	8	2
4	5	6	7	8	9	6	5	8	9	4	9

8	9	5	8	7	5	6	9	6	7	4	6
9	7	6	3	7	8	9	5	9	6	7	8

Single column addition to 10:

3	2	1	5	2	3	6	4	7	0	6	6
1	1	6	2	6	5	0	1	1	6	1	1
3	4	1	1	2	2	4	5	2	2	3	2

Single column addition to 10:

3	6	2	7	6	2	4	4	2	2	1	1
5	1	3	1	2	7	4	2	3	2	1	4
2	3	2	1	1	1	2	1	3	6	5	5

1	3	1	3	3	3	2	1	1	3	2	1
1	3	2	2	1	1	2	3	1	3	2	3
3	3	5	1	4	3	5	4	2	4	2	6

1	1	1	2	0	1	0	2	4	6	0	8
2	1	2	3	8	1	1	2	4	1	1	1
2	7	7	4	1	4	3	3	1	2	2	1

2	1	4	1	1	1	0	2	2	1	1	1
4	3	4	3	2	1	9	3	2	2	2	1
4	3	2	3	4	6	1	5	4	5	3	1

Double column addition to 19:

5	9	4	5	7	6	5	3	4	6	5	5
12	10	14	13	12	12	14	16	15	11	10	11

Double column addition to 99:

5	7	3	2	4	3	8	7	2	4	1	3
52	80	41	34	73	22	21	51	87	95	38	33

Double column addition to 99:

34	32	32	30	25	31	35	31	24	42	20	21
14	33	60	45	11	60	64	12	25	30	34	40

20	34	30	52	12	34	34	43	26	26	52	37
15	60	12	42	22	45	51	16	63	23	44	51

Situation Solving

1. Tony spent 3 h in Hairdressing on Monday, 2 h on Tuesday and 4 h on Wednesday. How many hours were spent in Hairdressing?

2. During the past year in Textiles Susan made an apron using 2 m of material, a skirt using 3 m and a dress using 5 m of material. How much material did she use during the year?

3. In the Motor Service shop John changed the oil in three cars. He used 3 L in the first, 2 L in the second and 3 L in the third. How much oil did he use?

4. Joe used 3 shovels of sand, 2 shovels of gravel and 2 shovels of cement to make concrete. How much material did he use?

5. The Bill of Material in Woodworking called for 1 m of maple, 4 m of pine and 3 m of mahogany. How many metres of material were used?

6. Jean made 36 sandwiches on Wednesday, 48 on Thursday and 12 on Friday. How many sandwiches were made?

7. Joyce typed letters in Office Practice. She did 2 the first hour, 1 the second hour and 5 the third hour. How many did she type?

4

Situation Solving

1. The cafeteria set out 16 desserts. They had to make 6 more. How many did they sell?

2. There were 2 cases of oil in the store room. One case held 15 L and the other held 7 L. How much oil was there?

3. The students laundered 47 shirts during the period. There were 6 shirts they were unable to complete. How many shirts did they have at the beginning of the period?

4. The Welding Shop produced 64 brackets on Friday. This was 8 less than they had hoped to produce. How many had they hoped to produce?

5. The Horticulture Shop sold 76 potted plants during the week. There were 9 plants not sold. How many plants did they have at the beginning of the week?

6. In Child Care Class there were 23 children registered on Monday. During the week 9 more were registered. How many children were registered by Friday?

7. Tom ordered 47 m of copper piping for the job. He found he needed 8 m more. How much pipe did the job require?

Situation Solving

1. In Tailoring Class the groups used 9 m, 3 m, 7 m and 8 m of material. How much material was used?

2. The Auto Body shop repaired 5 cars the first term, 6 the second term, 4 the third term and 9 the fourth term. How many cars were repaired during the year?

3. In one term the Merchandising Shop sold 5 school sweaters, 9 girl's rings, 7 boy's rings and 8 school crests. How many articles did they sell?

4. Class A produced 9 clay bowls, Class B produced 4, Class C produced 7 and Class D produced 6. How many clay bowls were produced in the Craft Room?

5. In Motor Servicing, the students replaced spark plugs in four cars. They used 8 plugs, 4 plugs, 6 plugs and 8 plugs. How many spark plugs did they use?

6. During the week the Metal Shop made screwdrivers for sale. They sold 9; 6 were left over, 4 were not suitable for sale and 5 were not completed. How many screwdrivers did the Shop make?

7. The Electrical Shop made extension cords. At the end of the period they had cords 5 m, 7 m, 8 m and 6 m long. How much material did they use?

Addition with carrying:

1.
8	9	8	7	9	6	0	8	5	2	4	3
35	23	23	58	89	18	38	49	56	69	78	29

2.
9	6	7	5	8	7	5	8	8	5	7	9
75	38	65	16	18	68	37	39	58	28	25	47

3.
39	12	16	37	43	79	45	24	27	68	28	48
32	29	79	67	29	24	57	79	75	34	63	47

4.
76	22	78	88	77	24	64	54	87	99	86	56
16	19	24	18	17	18	44	16	24	11	27	26

5.
66	87	44	55	75	76	97	77	87	88	66	57
25	13	28	28	25	25	25	16	16	23	19	18

6.
72	89	66	69	60	18	29	97	82	30	75	82
83	42	35	83	39	69	46	38	61	48	25	45
34	57	62	54	54	98	83	26	38	71	50	90

7.
21	25	46	37	34	34	47	36	45	36	38	85
34	48	58	15	69	19	23	23	38	29	16	25
52	43	14	28	85	23	87	18	19	57	44	29

8.
31	87	99	42	42	48	25	99	62	66	87	39
62	26	61	67	76	67	30	42	39	27	26	26
56	32	37	93	27	93	61	58	51	48	39	54

9.
64	87	43	58	93	39	56	83	48	92	54	92
26	26	62	67	46	56	92	26	36	96	26	72
93	43	93	26	62	82	67	54	92	37	89	68

1.
```
  23          12          34          21
  34          45          23          22
  10          32          42          25
 ───         ───         ───         ───
```

2.
```
  31          40          23          32
  35          22          35          41
  33          24          41          12
 ───         ───         ───         ───
```

3.
```
  73    24    62    63    63    63    84    42
  15    64    52    32    63    24    23    36
  31    41    31    24    31    62    52    61
 ───   ───   ───   ───   ───   ───   ───   ───
```

4.
```
  62    43    95    24    96    26    92    43
  32    23    51    31    50    43    52    42
  44    33    43    94    22    90    35    40
 ───   ───   ───   ───   ───   ───   ───   ───
```

5.
```
  62          33          42          64          42          36
  71          80          63          90          51          20
  83          46          31          34          63          30
  42          30          60          21          90          50
 ───         ───         ───         ───         ───         ───
```

6. $42 + 3 + 20 + 30 + 24 =$

7. $82 + 61 + 30 + 23 + 92 =$

8. $2 + 1 + 93 + 42 + 63 =$

9. $42 + 60 + 23 + 90 + 3 + 6 =$

10. $35 + 61 + 20 + 60 + 50 =$

11. $42 + 63 + 90 + 21 =$

12. $67 + 83 + 62 + 73 =$

13. $46 + 59 + 67 + 27 =$

14. $86 + 20 + 38 + 73 + 9 =$

15. $92 + 67 + 59 + 48 =$

16. $36 + 94 + 85 + 21 + 6 =$

17. $9 + 36 + 21 + 54 + 6 =$

18. $84 + 26 + 9 + 8 + 67 =$

19. $26 + 3 + 1 + 47 + 6 =$

Situation Solving

1. Maha used 27 h during Term One window cleaning and 45 h during Term Two. How many hours did she use during the two terms doing window cleaning?

2. Class B produced 37 patio stones and Class C produced 39. How many patio stones were produced by the two classes?

3. The Horticulture Shop sold 47 boxes of petunias and 39 boxes of marigolds. How many boxes of plants did they sell?

4. Betty uses 28 hair curlers and Jean uses 37. In all, how many curlers do they use?

5. The Electrical Shop repaired 58 small motors during Term One and 35 during Term Two. How many motors did they repair during the two terms?

6. Joe pressed 35 articles and Pete pressed 47 articles. How many articles were pressed?

7. The Textile Shop used 69 m of cotton and 37 m of denim. How many metres of material did they use?

Situation Solving

1. Tom can lay 23 tiles per hour, Dick can lay 34 and Bill can lay 24. How many tiles can the three boys lay in one hour?

2. Sue works in a restaurant. On Tuesday she served 23 people, on Wednesday 14 people and on Saturday 57 people. How many people did she serve in the three days?

3. Carrie pumps gasoline at the service station. On Tuesday she put gas in 26 cars, on Thursday 47 cars and on Saturday 89 cars. Into how many cars did she pump gas in the three days?

4. Jim delivers drugs in his spare time. During September he delivered 23 parcels to Front Street, 49 to East Street and 86 to Elm Street. How many parcels did he deliver?

5. George used 26 L of gas in one week, 39 L another week and 42 L in the third week. How many litres did he use in the three weeks?

6. The Food Shop had 23 guests in March, 36 in April and 32 guests in May. How many guests did they serve during the three months?

7. Joe sold 58 tickets to the dance, Bill sold 27 and Susan sold 38. How many tickets were sold by the three pupils?

1.

40	27	69	49	28	35	67	38	46	73	82	96
69	66	23	95	63	94	56	49	98	60	37	42
20	27	77	88	79	87	82	25	59	85	27	56
78	32	18	75	98	79	38	54	28	37	99	84
27	48	19	63	88	59	93	26	65	28	69	68

2.

27	83	71	60	37	32	69	43	45	15	77	98
63	39	42	73	82	96	28	39	27	77	62	18
18	65	91	82	68	20	66	86	94	67	49	66
76	98	85	82	99	88	56	74	89	40	58	16
49	16	21	72	17	71	38	56	94	62	18	74

3.

467	342	665	149	311	635
321	598	326	372	283	428
895	607	489	680	572	976

4.

869	469	683	842	780	369
426	932	334	769	931	624
392	468	401	368	720	396

5.

8 364	3 742	3 974	7 684
3 874	9 839	4 838	9 382
9 762	2 647	7 896	9 476

6.

7 896	3 874	7 842	3 896
3 894	9 287	3 948	4 792
4 378	6 342	7 463	6 384

7.

3 086	3 804	8 096	8 764
4 970	9 780	9 480	9 806
7 809	7 039	7 907	8 049

8.

6 273	4 639	2 679	8 367
9 304	2 783	3 486	9 276
8 726	5 906	5 200	4 536

Situation Solving

1. The class made candy for a sale. They made 412 pieces of fudge and 799 pieces of white candy. How many pieces of candy did they make?

2. The students planted 497 tulip bulbs and 647 daffodil bulbs. How many bulbs did they plant?

3. The Woodworking Shop ordered 378 m of pine, 296 m of basswood and 163 m of mahogany. How much wood did they order?

4. The Food Shop used 186 kg of flour in March, 264 kg in April and 194 kg in May. How much flour did they use?

5. During the year the Merchandising Shop sold 264 crests, 124 pens, 268 pkg. of paper and 183 erasers. How many articles did they sell?

6. The Welding Shop had 253 kg of scrap during Term One, 156 kg during Term Two, 320 during Term Three and 258 during Term Four. How much scrap did they have during the year?

7. During the day the Service Station pumped 465 L, 532 L, 193 L, 635 L and 473 L. How many litres of gasoline did they pump?

Adding dollars and cents:

1. $0.35 $1.22 $3.20 $0.40 $0.31

$0.35	$1.22	$3.20	$0.40	$0.31
0.26	0.36	0.42	5.03	0.35
0.30	0.41	0.36	0.16	4.23

2.

$0.63	$0.42	$0.73	$0.62	$0.41	$0.93
0.81	0.73	0.52	0.60	0.09	0.72
0.30	0.32	0.83	0.06	0.50	0.60
0.22	0.61	0.31	0.43	0.60	0.42

3.

$2.73	$4.59	$4.93	$2.46	$6.25	$6.30
4.28	5.62	2.75	0.09	8.46	0.48
3.90	5.05	9.38	5.89	9.53	6.59

4.

$0.06	$9.25	$4.26	$4.50	$2.45
1.25	3.80	3.05	3.60	0.26
0.60	0.20	2.98	2.48	3.98
6.75	0.06	1.40	5.93	2.99

5. $2.26 + $0.06 + $2.85 + $0.76 + $3.98 =

6. $6.26 + $4.98 + $3.25 + $0.06 =

7. $6.30 + $9.42 + $0.14 + $0.98 =

8. $2.00 + $3.96 + $0.32 + $0.64 + $3.00 =

9. $0.34 + $2.60 + $8.64 + $0.06 + $4.80 =

10. $2.62 + $0.39 + $9.60 + $36.50 =

11. $32.56 + $2.96 + $0.05 + $3.56 + $4.50 =

12. $9.26 + $4.06 + $0.26 + $5.68 + $9.36 =

13. $8.50 + $2.39 + $9.21 + $6.36 =

14. $9.20 + $0.33 + $0.04 + $26.56 =

15. $5.20 + $9.36 + $4.25 + $0.45 =

16. $4.55 + $6.93 + $6.06 + $9.20 + $3.80 =

17. $5.86 + $0.04 + $2.56 + $9.26 + $5.84 =

18. $5.56 + $19.26 + $9.36 + $81.56 + $8.21 =

19. $14.27 + $0.27 + $0.04 + $9.26 + $18.93 =

20. $0.56 + $191.65 + $3.21 + $9.04 =

Situation Solving

Work Here

1. At lunch, Bill spent 99¢ for a hamburger, 40¢ for French fries and 65¢ for a milk shake. How much did he spend?

2. One evening John spent $3.25 for a movie, $1.60 for food, and $1.00 for transportation. How much did he spend?

3. Carmen bought a ring for $14.95, a school crest for $1.75 and a school sweater for $12.95. How much did she spend?

4. Eugene worked at the corner grocery store after school. On Monday he made $2.52, Wednesday $3.56 and Saturday $7.02. What were his earnings?

5. A family liked to have take-out food once a month. The bill for September was $12.65, for October $16.50, November $11.35 and December $10.75. What was the total cost for 4 months?

6. During the last month Tom spent $14.96, $6.72 and $7.48 on minor car repairs. What was his bill?

7. Sally spent $14.98 for a sweater, $16.96 for a skirt and $28.98 for shoes. How much did she spend for clothes?

Situation Solving

Work Here

8. One week a family spent $23.46, $28.49 and $16.07 on groceries. How much did they spend for groceries during the week?

9. Mr. Karo spent $31.50 for a new tire, $17.59 for repairs and $15.56 for gasoline. How much did he spend?

10. John kept track of his lawn maintenance expenses for the month. He spent $1.29 for gasoline, $2.59 for weed spray, $4.98 for a new rake, $2.50 for blade sharpening, $15.99 for a hose and $12.98 for fertilizer. What were his expenses for the month?

11. Paul was redecorating his living room. He spent $38.98 for paint, $28.85 for rug cleaning and $22.87 for curtain cleaning. How much did it cost to redecorate the room?

12. Eugene built a recreation room. He spent $82.50 for floor tile, $179.89 for ceiling tile and $209.98 for wall panelling. How much did it cost him to build the room?

13. Don Clark is a traveller for a clothing store. His expenses for the month were as follows: gasoline $180.90, food $178.65, motel bills $340.00 and miscellaneous expenses $133.45. What were his travelling expenses for the month?

15

Subtraction

Subtraction facts to 9:

9	8	7	6	5	4	3	9	7	6	4	8
−2	−5	−4	−6	−3	−4	−0	−5	−7	−4	−2	−3

8	7	5	1	7	9	2	9	6	3	6	8
−7	−5	−2	−0	−3	−1	−2	−8	−2	−3	−5	−4

0	9	7	6	4	5	9	2	9	8	5	8
−0	−4	−2	−1	−0	−5	−7	−0	−3	−6	−4	−2

9	7	6	9	3	8	8	5	7	1	6	4
−6	−6	−3	−9	−2	−1	−8	−1	−0	−1	−0	−3

Subtraction facts 11 to 19 with no borrowing:

19	17	15	11	16	18	13	19	17	14	12	16
−6	−5	−3	−0	−5	−7	−2	−0	−2	−3	−1	−0

11	19	16	19	15	13	17	12	18	17	12	14
−1	−5	−3	−3	−4	−1	−4	−0	−3	−6	−2	−1

15	14	19	18	15	16	18	19	16	13	18	19
−2	−4	−7	−6	−1	−2	−8	−2	−6	−3	−4	−1

19	18	16	14	19	17	15	17	18	17	15	14
−9	−5	−4	−0	−4	−7	−0	−3	−2	−0	−5	−2

Subtraction facts to 100 with no borrowing:

93	17	23	38	45	76	89	79	91	82	81	76
−1	−5	−2	−6	−3	−4	−7	−8	−0	−1	−0	−3

52	94	63	47	89	48	39	28	66	47	58	24
−0	−3	−1	−6	−5	−7	−8	−4	−2	−1	−6	−0

Subtraction (no borrowing):

1.
85	96	79	67	59	48
−3	−4	−7	−3	−8	−6

2.
87	69	48	73	62	94
−6	−3	−2	−1	−2	−2

3.
75	86	98	76	69	95
−32	−32	−45	−54	−45	−64

4.
87	50	97	68	73	64
−72	−30	−11	−14	−42	−20

5.
324	690	198	948	726	246
−14	−70	−72	−327	−604	−120

6.
897	643	206	493	728	489
−273	−421	−104	−302	−420	−314

7.
1 826	4 998	7 646	9 486	7 250	4 060
−204	−3 220	−2 140	−2 301	−6 030	−1 030

8.
6 724	8 463	3 094	5 836	9 930	4 862
−210	−7 121	−1 072	−1 210	−1 210	−1 321

9.
44 896	38 649	86 432	46 325	53 929	43 982
−10 212	−1 427	−11 020	−11 024	−32 701	−21 170

Situation Solving

Work Here

1. The Textile Shop bought 18 m of cotton. The students used 5 m. How much was left?

2. An order was sent to the Welding Shop for 26 book ends. The students made 5. How many more had to be made?

3. The Cafeteria made 69 sandwiches for lunch. They had 7 left at the end of lunch. How many did they sell?

4. One week Motor Servicing had a work order for 36 lubrications. By Wednesday they had completed 21. How many still had to be done?

5. Office Practice had 49 letters to type during the week. They still had 16 to do on Friday. How many had they completed?

6. An order was sent to the Horticultural Shop for 96 boxes of plants. They were able to supply all but 14 boxes. How many were they able to supply?

7. Ken bought 78 bottles of soft drinks for the party. If 56 bottles were used, how many were left?

Subtraction with borrowing:

1.
23	48	77	42	10	44
−7	−9	−8	−6	−3	−7

2.
75	89	46	23	64	51
−8	−9	−7	−8	−9	−5

3.
86	74	98	45	57	33
−28	−35	−59	−19	−23	−15

4.
389	785	321	274	789	585
−69	−58	−19	−59	−39	−26

5.
734	803	736	572	391	835
−218	−209	−518	−209	−218	−228

6.
829	737	291	894	645	738
−209	−518	−178	−379	−129	−519

7.
4 796	4 892	7 825	6 942	3 084	7 295
−1 569	−347	−3 817	−1 007	−39	−5 168

8.
6 793	9 273	4 436	8 469	4 267	4 583
−4 362	−1 486	−267	−2 737	−1 032	−1 309

9.
2 654	43 876	84 653	48 697	48 672	98 326
−1 659	−12 764	−16 179	−21 139	−19 727	−14 327

1.	843 −572	857 −382	938 −246	958 −273	625 −281	738 −396
2.	674 −182	765 −483	918 −294	749 −478	555 −281	624 −161
3.	747 −278	631 −149	957 −369	726 −258	958 −459	484 −289
4.	826 −593	769 −398	923 −458	543 −176	676 −189	831 −242
5.	2 867 −1 089	4 860 −1 249	6 989 −299	4 326 −2 139	6 048 −1 039	2 489 −299
6.	9 870 −1 389	8 403 −2 197	6 426 −1 379	8 646 −2 399	2 943 −467	8 693 −1 293
7.	5 216 −1 087	4 613 −1 245	18 496 −3 199	9 363 −1 194	8 962 −1 293	3 261 −1 084
8.	6 767 −1 496	4 326 −2 405	9 506 −2 768	4 367 −1 267	9 356 −2 509	8 522 −6 392
9.	4 567 −3 296	8 672 −1 396	9 676 −9 137	82 671 −8 139	5 637 −2 962	5 397 −2 698

1. $\begin{array}{r} 46 \\ -29 \\ \hline \end{array}$ $\begin{array}{r} 374 \\ -196 \\ \hline \end{array}$ $\begin{array}{r} 4\ 846 \\ -1\ 978 \\ \hline \end{array}$ $\begin{array}{r} 3\ 842 \\ -1\ 895 \\ \hline \end{array}$ $\begin{array}{r} 3\ 072 \\ -1\ 895 \\ \hline \end{array}$ $\begin{array}{r} 2\ 842 \\ -1\ 394 \\ \hline \end{array}$

2. $\begin{array}{r} 568 \\ -289 \\ \hline \end{array}$ $\begin{array}{r} 6\ 357 \\ -4\ 598 \\ \hline \end{array}$ $\begin{array}{r} 795 \\ -296 \\ \hline \end{array}$ $\begin{array}{r} 5\ 432 \\ -2\ 876 \\ \hline \end{array}$ $\begin{array}{r} 281 \\ -195 \\ \hline \end{array}$ $\begin{array}{r} 3\ 916 \\ -1\ 297 \\ \hline \end{array}$

3. $\begin{array}{r} 3\ 264 \\ -1\ 496 \\ \hline \end{array}$ $\begin{array}{r} 5\ 148 \\ -4\ 287 \\ \hline \end{array}$ $\begin{array}{r} 9\ 843 \\ -3\ 957 \\ \hline \end{array}$ $\begin{array}{r} 4\ 139 \\ -2\ 978 \\ \hline \end{array}$ $\begin{array}{r} 6\ 527 \\ -4\ 938 \\ \hline \end{array}$ $\begin{array}{r} 3\ 485 \\ -1\ 807 \\ \hline \end{array}$

4. $\begin{array}{r} 2\ 007 \\ -1\ 348 \\ \hline \end{array}$ $\begin{array}{r} 2\ 000 \\ -1\ 874 \\ \hline \end{array}$ $\begin{array}{r} 9\ 756 \\ -2\ 859 \\ \hline \end{array}$ $\begin{array}{r} 7\ 892 \\ -5\ 999 \\ \hline \end{array}$ $\begin{array}{r} 4\ 906 \\ -2\ 798 \\ \hline \end{array}$ $\begin{array}{r} 3\ 428 \\ -1\ 090 \\ \hline \end{array}$

5. $\begin{array}{r} 2\ 897 \\ -1\ 809 \\ \hline \end{array}$ $\begin{array}{r} 7\ 894 \\ -4\ 997 \\ \hline \end{array}$ $\begin{array}{r} 2\ 096 \\ -1\ 877 \\ \hline \end{array}$ $\begin{array}{r} 4\ 897 \\ -2\ 898 \\ \hline \end{array}$ $\begin{array}{r} 2\ 485 \\ -1\ 976 \\ \hline \end{array}$ $\begin{array}{r} 3\ 875 \\ -1\ 909 \\ \hline \end{array}$

6. $\begin{array}{r} 8\ 095 \\ -2\ 998 \\ \hline \end{array}$ $\begin{array}{r} 3\ 896 \\ -1\ 988 \\ \hline \end{array}$ $\begin{array}{r} 4\ 090 \\ -2\ 653 \\ \hline \end{array}$ $\begin{array}{r} 4\ 000 \\ -2\ 254 \\ \hline \end{array}$ $\begin{array}{r} 5\ 563 \\ -2\ 978 \\ \hline \end{array}$ $\begin{array}{r} 4\ 394 \\ -3\ 007 \\ \hline \end{array}$

7. $\begin{array}{r} 5\ 090 \\ -3\ 993 \\ \hline \end{array}$ $\begin{array}{r} 7\ 890 \\ -1\ 985 \\ \hline \end{array}$ $\begin{array}{r} 7\ 568 \\ -3\ 889 \\ \hline \end{array}$ $\begin{array}{r} 2\ 940 \\ -1\ 761 \\ \hline \end{array}$ $\begin{array}{r} 3\ 886 \\ -1\ 977 \\ \hline \end{array}$ $\begin{array}{r} 4\ 000 \\ -2\ 894 \\ \hline \end{array}$

8. $\begin{array}{r} 3\ 096 \\ -2\ 199 \\ \hline \end{array}$ $\begin{array}{r} 8\ 306 \\ -1\ 492 \\ \hline \end{array}$ $\begin{array}{r} 5\ 263 \\ -1\ 278 \\ \hline \end{array}$ $\begin{array}{r} 4\ 430 \\ -2\ 106 \\ \hline \end{array}$ $\begin{array}{r} 9\ 006 \\ -2\ 939 \\ \hline \end{array}$ $\begin{array}{r} 8\ 050 \\ -2\ 909 \\ \hline \end{array}$

9. $\begin{array}{r} 4\ 523 \\ -6\ 267 \\ \hline \end{array}$ $\begin{array}{r} 4\ 623 \\ -9\ 076 \\ \hline \end{array}$ $\begin{array}{r} 4\ 806 \\ -2\ 997 \\ \hline \end{array}$ $\begin{array}{r} 3\ 600 \\ -1\ 929 \\ \hline \end{array}$ $\begin{array}{r} 3\ 205 \\ -1\ 099 \\ \hline \end{array}$ $\begin{array}{r} 8\ 600 \\ -3\ 979 \\ \hline \end{array}$

Situation Solving

1. During the term Auto Body had 16 cars to repair. By mid-term they had completed 9. How many did they still have to repair?

2. The Hairdressing Shop ordered 24 bottles of shampoo. When they took inventory they had 7 bottles left. How many bottles of shampoo did they use?

3. A piecework sewer made 66 blouses in 1 day. All were done correctly except 9. How many were accepted by the company?

4. The Building Maintenance Shop had 74 windows to wash in the school. By the end of the day they had 9 left to do. How many windows did they wash during the day?

5. Of the 24 students in the Woodworking Shop 8 had completed their projects. How many still had to complete their projects?

6. A laundry worker had 82 shirts to launder. She completed all but 7. How many had she done?

7. 43 sweaters were purchased by the School Store and 9 were left at the end of the year. How many sweaters were sold?

22

Situation Solving

Work Here

1. Susan made 74 sandwiches for a senior citizens' party. After the party 17 were left. How many were eaten?

2. John had 97 tiles to lay to complete a floor. By noon he had laid 39. How many tiles did he have to lay in the afternoon to finish the job?

3. Tom made 56 deliveries and Susan made 39. How many more deliveries did Tom make than Susan?

4. Mary read 58 pages in her book. If the book had 96 pages, how many more did she have to read?

5. Betty baked 51 tarts and Joe baked 24. How many more tarts did Betty bake than Joe?

6. The Tailoring Shop ordered 53 spools of thread. At the end of the term they had 27 spools left. How many spools of thread did they use?

7. The Horticulture Shop planted 83 small trees and shrubs around the school. 19 died during the winter. How many lived?

23

Situation Solving

Work Here

1. Brian has 137 papers to deliver each day. Yesterday he delivered 109 by five o'clock. How many did he still have to deliver?

2. Sue's father allows her to drive 487 km a month. During the first three weeks she drove 239 km. How many km can she drive during the last week?

3. Last year the local basketball team scored 486 points. This year they scored 523 points. How many more points did they score this year than last year?

4. The granary on the farm holds 3 852 bushels. A total of 2 976 bushels of grain were put in. How many more bushels will the granary hold?

5. Last year Smith's apple orchard harvested 2 976 apples. This year they harvested 3 254 apples. How many more apples were harvested this year than last year?

6. The Thames Conservation Area had 782 campers in 1954, 1 572 in 1964, and 5 361 in 1974.
   (a) How many more campers were there in 1964 than in 1954?
   (b) How many more campers were there in 1974 than in 1964?
   (c) How many more campers were there in 1974 than in 1954?

Subtraction — dollars and cents:

1.
$9.46	$3.48	$8.76	$6.95	$4.95	$14.90
−0.21	−1.20	−2.41	−4.23	−3.74	−1.30

2.
$14.63	$21.36	$89.56	$136.49	$276.50	$463.89
−3.21	−10.30	−34.24	−11.41	−65.10	−32.73

3.
$6.51	$9.74	$86.65	$7.28	$4.30	$3.06
−2.31	−1.62	−3.04	−0.28	−4.10	−2.01

4.
$8.64	$943.43	$77.58	$9.63	$4.29	$3.08
−3.75	−42.88	−1.99	−2.68	−1.49	−1.79

5.
$23.96	$87.50	$59.64	$74.84	$58.61	$29.20
−19.61	−9.68	−49.78	−8.93	−29.87	−19.37

6.
$79.80	$78.46	$94.75	$ 72.01	$79.06	$55.87
−3.47	−8.54	−8.70	−56.22	−4.79	−46.84

7.
$91.50	$52.41	$62.92	$84.82	$72.81	$41.36
−47.29	−14.63	−13.95	−27.88	−27.81	−14.88

8.
$469.62	$389.46	$864.93	$462.50	$5 678.92	$4 567.08
−53.09	−129.67	−210.99	−129.89	−390.99	−1 297.38

9.
$4 693.56	$4 862.00	$8 265.37	$5 867.29	$8 646.56	$2 659.38
−1 162.92	−1 296.59	−2 136.59	−5 210.03	−2 139.38	−1 923.05

Situation Solving

1. Bob's allowance is $7.50. He spent $2.20. How much did he have left?

2. Bobby earned 85¢ babysitting. She had 8¢ left after buying lipstick. How much was the lipstick?

3. Terry's allowance is $11.75. If he spent $3.59 and saved the rest, how much did he save?

4. While babysitting Carol earned $9.25. If she spent $6.39 for a birthday present, how much did she have left?

5. A radio costs $19.83 at the department store and $16.99 in the hardware store. How much could be saved by buying at the hardware store?

6. The Students' Council spent $87.50 preparing for their dance. They took in $147.50 at the door. How much did they make at the dance?

7. Last week Bradley earned $10.85 raking leaves and cutting lawns. This week he earned $9.96. How much more did he make last week than this week?

Situation Solving

8. Andy wanted to save $149.00 for a new suit. He now has $69.96. How much more must he save before he can buy the suit?

9. A new T.V. sells for $559.95 cash, or $608.00 if bought on the instalment plan. How much can be saved by paying cash?

10. The price of a new car was $5 185.00. The same car at a different dealer cost $4 998.05. How much could be saved by buying the car from the second dealer?

11. The sewing class paid $36.85 for material from the wholesale supplier. If the class had bought the same material at the store they would have paid $49.70. How much did they save by buying the material from the wholesale supplier?

12. The Smiths' grocery bill was $223.00 for September, $217.86 for October, and $209.97 for November.

    (a) How much more was the bill in September than in October?

    (b) How much more was the bill in October than in November?

    (c) How much more was the bill in September than in November?

Multiplication

$1 \times 1 = 1$	$2 \times 1 = 2$	$3 \times 1 = 3$
$1 \times 2 = 2$	$2 \times 2 = 4$	$3 \times 2 = 6$
$1 \times 3 = 3$	$2 \times 3 = 6$	$3 \times 3 = 9$
$1 \times 4 = 4$	$2 \times 4 = 8$	$3 \times 4 = 12$
$1 \times 5 = 5$	$2 \times 5 = 10$	$3 \times 5 = 15$
$1 \times 6 = 6$	$2 \times 6 = 12$	$3 \times 6 = 18$
$1 \times 7 = 7$	$2 \times 7 = 14$	$3 \times 7 = 21$
$1 \times 8 = 8$	$2 \times 8 = 16$	$3 \times 8 = 24$
$1 \times 9 = 9$	$2 \times 9 = 18$	$3 \times 9 = 27$

$4 \times 1 = 4$	$5 \times 1 = 5$	$6 \times 1 = 6$
$4 \times 2 = 8$	$5 \times 2 = 10$	$6 \times 2 = 12$
$4 \times 3 = 12$	$5 \times 3 = 15$	$6 \times 3 = 18$
$4 \times 4 = 16$	$5 \times 4 = 20$	$6 \times 4 = 24$
$4 \times 5 = 20$	$5 \times 5 = 25$	$6 \times 5 = 30$
$4 \times 6 = 24$	$5 \times 6 = 30$	$6 \times 6 = 36$
$4 \times 7 = 28$	$5 \times 7 = 35$	$6 \times 7 = 42$
$4 \times 8 = 32$	$5 \times 8 = 40$	$6 \times 8 = 48$
$4 \times 9 = 36$	$5 \times 9 = 45$	$6 \times 9 = 54$

$7 \times 1 = 7$	$8 \times 1 = 8$	$9 \times 1 = 9$
$7 \times 2 = 14$	$8 \times 2 = 16$	$9 \times 2 = 18$
$7 \times 3 = 21$	$8 \times 3 = 24$	$9 \times 3 = 27$
$7 \times 4 = 28$	$8 \times 4 = 32$	$9 \times 4 = 36$
$7 \times 5 = 35$	$8 \times 5 = 40$	$9 \times 5 = 45$
$7 \times 6 = 42$	$8 \times 6 = 48$	$9 \times 6 = 54$
$7 \times 7 = 49$	$8 \times 7 = 56$	$9 \times 7 = 63$
$7 \times 8 = 56$	$8 \times 8 = 64$	$9 \times 8 = 72$
$7 \times 9 = 63$	$8 \times 9 = 72$	$9 \times 9 = 81$

Multiplication with no carrying:

1. $\begin{array}{r}9\\ \times2\\ \hline\end{array}$ $\begin{array}{r}5\\ \times2\\ \hline\end{array}$ $\begin{array}{r}8\\ \times2\\ \hline\end{array}$ $\begin{array}{r}6\\ \times2\\ \hline\end{array}$ $\begin{array}{r}2\\ \times2\\ \hline\end{array}$ $\begin{array}{r}9\\ \times2\\ \hline\end{array}$ $\begin{array}{r}4\\ \times2\\ \hline\end{array}$ $\begin{array}{r}7\\ \times2\\ \hline\end{array}$ $\begin{array}{r}3\\ \times2\\ \hline\end{array}$ $\begin{array}{r}1\\ \times2\\ \hline\end{array}$ $\begin{array}{r}5\\ \times2\\ \hline\end{array}$ $\begin{array}{r}0\\ \times2\\ \hline\end{array}$

2. $\begin{array}{r}8\\ \times3\\ \hline\end{array}$ $\begin{array}{r}4\\ \times3\\ \hline\end{array}$ $\begin{array}{r}7\\ \times3\\ \hline\end{array}$ $\begin{array}{r}5\\ \times3\\ \hline\end{array}$ $\begin{array}{r}6\\ \times3\\ \hline\end{array}$ $\begin{array}{r}0\\ \times3\\ \hline\end{array}$ $\begin{array}{r}3\\ \times3\\ \hline\end{array}$ $\begin{array}{r}9\\ \times3\\ \hline\end{array}$ $\begin{array}{r}1\\ \times3\\ \hline\end{array}$ $\begin{array}{r}3\\ \times3\\ \hline\end{array}$ $\begin{array}{r}6\\ \times3\\ \hline\end{array}$ $\begin{array}{r}8\\ \times3\\ \hline\end{array}$

3. $\begin{array}{r}8\\ \times4\\ \hline\end{array}$ $\begin{array}{r}5\\ \times4\\ \hline\end{array}$ $\begin{array}{r}7\\ \times4\\ \hline\end{array}$ $\begin{array}{r}1\\ \times4\\ \hline\end{array}$ $\begin{array}{r}3\\ \times4\\ \hline\end{array}$ $\begin{array}{r}0\\ \times4\\ \hline\end{array}$ $\begin{array}{r}6\\ \times4\\ \hline\end{array}$ $\begin{array}{r}2\\ \times4\\ \hline\end{array}$ $\begin{array}{r}4\\ \times4\\ \hline\end{array}$ $\begin{array}{r}9\\ \times4\\ \hline\end{array}$ $\begin{array}{r}1\\ \times4\\ \hline\end{array}$ $\begin{array}{r}5\\ \times4\\ \hline\end{array}$

4. $\begin{array}{r}0\\ \times5\\ \hline\end{array}$ $\begin{array}{r}4\\ \times5\\ \hline\end{array}$ $\begin{array}{r}3\\ \times5\\ \hline\end{array}$ $\begin{array}{r}8\\ \times5\\ \hline\end{array}$ $\begin{array}{r}6\\ \times5\\ \hline\end{array}$ $\begin{array}{r}1\\ \times5\\ \hline\end{array}$ $\begin{array}{r}9\\ \times5\\ \hline\end{array}$ $\begin{array}{r}7\\ \times5\\ \hline\end{array}$ $\begin{array}{r}2\\ \times5\\ \hline\end{array}$ $\begin{array}{r}5\\ \times5\\ \hline\end{array}$ $\begin{array}{r}7\\ \times5\\ \hline\end{array}$ $\begin{array}{r}9\\ \times5\\ \hline\end{array}$

5. $\begin{array}{r}8\\ \times6\\ \hline\end{array}$ $\begin{array}{r}5\\ \times6\\ \hline\end{array}$ $\begin{array}{r}2\\ \times6\\ \hline\end{array}$ $\begin{array}{r}0\\ \times6\\ \hline\end{array}$ $\begin{array}{r}3\\ \times6\\ \hline\end{array}$ $\begin{array}{r}6\\ \times6\\ \hline\end{array}$ $\begin{array}{r}4\\ \times6\\ \hline\end{array}$ $\begin{array}{r}1\\ \times6\\ \hline\end{array}$ $\begin{array}{r}9\\ \times6\\ \hline\end{array}$ $\begin{array}{r}6\\ \times6\\ \hline\end{array}$ $\begin{array}{r}2\\ \times6\\ \hline\end{array}$ $\begin{array}{r}4\\ \times6\\ \hline\end{array}$

6. $\begin{array}{r}9\\ \times7\\ \hline\end{array}$ $\begin{array}{r}1\\ \times7\\ \hline\end{array}$ $\begin{array}{r}5\\ \times7\\ \hline\end{array}$ $\begin{array}{r}0\\ \times7\\ \hline\end{array}$ $\begin{array}{r}6\\ \times7\\ \hline\end{array}$ $\begin{array}{r}2\\ \times7\\ \hline\end{array}$ $\begin{array}{r}8\\ \times7\\ \hline\end{array}$ $\begin{array}{r}3\\ \times7\\ \hline\end{array}$ $\begin{array}{r}7\\ \times7\\ \hline\end{array}$ $\begin{array}{r}4\\ \times7\\ \hline\end{array}$ $\begin{array}{r}0\\ \times7\\ \hline\end{array}$ $\begin{array}{r}6\\ \times7\\ \hline\end{array}$

7. $\begin{array}{r}5\\ \times8\\ \hline\end{array}$ $\begin{array}{r}1\\ \times8\\ \hline\end{array}$ $\begin{array}{r}9\\ \times8\\ \hline\end{array}$ $\begin{array}{r}3\\ \times8\\ \hline\end{array}$ $\begin{array}{r}7\\ \times8\\ \hline\end{array}$ $\begin{array}{r}0\\ \times8\\ \hline\end{array}$ $\begin{array}{r}5\\ \times8\\ \hline\end{array}$ $\begin{array}{r}6\\ \times8\\ \hline\end{array}$ $\begin{array}{r}2\\ \times8\\ \hline\end{array}$ $\begin{array}{r}8\\ \times8\\ \hline\end{array}$ $\begin{array}{r}4\\ \times8\\ \hline\end{array}$ $\begin{array}{r}8\\ \times8\\ \hline\end{array}$

8. $\begin{array}{r}1\\ \times9\\ \hline\end{array}$ $\begin{array}{r}4\\ \times9\\ \hline\end{array}$ $\begin{array}{r}9\\ \times9\\ \hline\end{array}$ $\begin{array}{r}7\\ \times9\\ \hline\end{array}$ $\begin{array}{r}5\\ \times9\\ \hline\end{array}$ $\begin{array}{r}0\\ \times9\\ \hline\end{array}$ $\begin{array}{r}6\\ \times9\\ \hline\end{array}$ $\begin{array}{r}2\\ \times9\\ \hline\end{array}$ $\begin{array}{r}8\\ \times9\\ \hline\end{array}$ $\begin{array}{r}3\\ \times9\\ \hline\end{array}$ $\begin{array}{r}9\\ \times9\\ \hline\end{array}$ $\begin{array}{r}7\\ \times9\\ \hline\end{array}$

9. $\begin{array}{r}31\\ \times6\\ \hline\end{array}$ $\begin{array}{r}23\\ \times3\\ \hline\end{array}$ $\begin{array}{r}10\\ \times9\\ \hline\end{array}$ $\begin{array}{r}13\\ \times2\\ \hline\end{array}$ $\begin{array}{r}94\\ \times2\\ \hline\end{array}$ $\begin{array}{r}81\\ \times8\\ \hline\end{array}$ $\begin{array}{r}73\\ \times2\\ \hline\end{array}$ $\begin{array}{r}64\\ \times1\\ \hline\end{array}$ $\begin{array}{r}92\\ \times4\\ \hline\end{array}$ $\begin{array}{r}71\\ \times7\\ \hline\end{array}$ $\begin{array}{r}32\\ \times4\\ \hline\end{array}$ $\begin{array}{r}51\\ \times6\\ \hline\end{array}$

10. $\begin{array}{r}72\\ \times4\\ \hline\end{array}$ $\begin{array}{r}56\\ \times1\\ \hline\end{array}$ $\begin{array}{r}42\\ \times3\\ \hline\end{array}$ $\begin{array}{r}91\\ \times8\\ \hline\end{array}$ $\begin{array}{r}64\\ \times2\\ \hline\end{array}$ $\begin{array}{r}83\\ \times3\\ \hline\end{array}$ $\begin{array}{r}62\\ \times1\\ \hline\end{array}$ $\begin{array}{r}93\\ \times3\\ \hline\end{array}$ $\begin{array}{r}63\\ \times2\\ \hline\end{array}$ $\begin{array}{r}43\\ \times3\\ \hline\end{array}$ $\begin{array}{r}53\\ \times3\\ \hline\end{array}$ $\begin{array}{r}66\\ \times1\\ \hline\end{array}$

Multiplying by 2 — 3 — 4:

1. 82×2 64×2 13×4 98×2 69×4 63×3

2. 83×2 24×4 72×3 94×2 57×4 23×2

3. 50×3 88×4 76×2 90×4 21×3 68×3

4. 60×3 97×2 87×4 98×3 60×4 53×2

5. 412×3 689×2 920×3 325×4 648×2 803×4

6. 813×3 798×4 357×2 903×2 611×3 614×4

7. 610×3 827×2 873×4 946×3 954×4 786×3

8. 367×2 269×3 483×4 527×2 365×4 494×3

9. $5\,629 \times 3$ $3\,972 \times 2$ $8\,425 \times 4$ $3\,066 \times 2$ $4\,837 \times 3$ $9\,624 \times 3$

Situation Solving

1. The 23 students in the Welding Shop each produced 3 towel racks. How many towel racks were produced?

2. There are 32 books on one shelf. How many books would there be on 2 shelves?

3. Julia found she could lay 22 tiles an hour. How many tiles could she lay in 4 h?

4. Pete sold 15 tickets to the dance. Jane sold 5 times as many. How many tickets did Jane sell?

5. The food school had on the average 37 guests a month. How many guests would they have in 2 months?

6. The Bill of Material for a project in Woodworking requires 3 m of pine. How much wood would be required to make 24 projects?

7. It takes 23 min to give a haircut. How long would it take to give 4 haircuts?

8. There are 24 cans of corn in a case. How many cans are there in 4 cases?

31

Multiplying by 5 — 6 — 7:

1. 17 ×5	38 ×6	29 ×7	60 ×5	49 ×6	58 ×7
2. 71 ×5	69 ×6	50 ×7	28 ×5	36 ×6	47 ×6
3. 93 ×7	72 ×5	61 ×6	80 ×5	48 ×7	59 ×6
4. 945 ×6	877 ×5	308 ×7	216 ×5	963 ×7	195 ×6
5. 973 ×5	892 ×6	862 ×7	974 ×6	541 ×5	530 ×7
6. 860 ×6	149 ×7	829 ×5	386 ×7	777 ×6	505 ×7
7. 749 ×6	837 ×7	290 ×6	816 ×5	405 ×6	739 ×7
8. 3 679 ×7	4 626 ×6	3 920 ×5	4 867 ×5	6 842 ×7	3 927 ×6
9. 4 686 ×6	5 326 ×5	9 378 ×7	4 922 ×7	8 673 ×5	4 237 ×6

Multiplying by 8 — 9:

1. 73 ×8	61 ×9	90 ×9	49 ×8	82 ×8	58 ×9
2. 81 ×9	60 ×8	52 ×8	73 ×9	43 ×9	42 ×8
3. 38 ×8	27 ×9	91 ×9	59 ×8	68 ×8	40 ×9
4. 839 ×9	178 ×8	297 ×9	442 ×8	560 ×8	563 ×9
5. 563 ×8	141 ×9	406 ×8	729 ×9	873 ×8	809 ×9
6. 726 ×9	804 ×9	319 ×8	296 ×9	755 ×8	180 ×8
7. 453 ×8	734 ×8	262 ×9	819 ×9	908 ×8	497 ×9
8. 3 967 ×8	8 462 ×9	4 053 ×9	6 278 ×8	3 005 ×8	9 276 ×9
9. 4 326 ×9	8 467 ×8	9 973 ×9	2 657 ×9	8 392 ×8	4 865 ×9

Situation Solving

1. How many things are there in 8 dozen?

2. It took 5 boys 37 min to wash the windows in the classroom. How long would it take one boy to do the job?

3. Each tray of sandwiches holds 47. How many sandwiches were served if 7 trays were used?

4. The Merchandising Shop sold an average of 29 school crests a week. How many would be sold in 6 weeks?

5. In one week Alice changed the oil in 36 cars. If each car required 3 L of oil, how much oil did she use?

6. Each class sold 58 tickets to the dance. How many tickets were sold by 7 classes?

7. Each of 9 boys delivered 75 handbills. How many handbills in all did they deliver?

8. The boys planted 89 bulbs a day for 8 days. How many bulbs did the boys plant?

Situation Solving

1. Danita drove 209 km each day for 5 days. How far did she travel in 5 days?

2. The Auto Service Shop services 237 cars a month. How many cars can be serviced in 9 months?

3. Ray attends North Vocational School and works for Acme Dairy in his spare time. He delivers 287 L of milk a day. How much milk does he deliver in 6 days?

4. The Carpentry Shop uses 874 m of pine each term. How much material would be required for 4 terms?

5. An airplane can travel 1 850 km/h. How many km could the plane travel in 8 h?

6. Jay worked part time as a farmer's helper during the summer. He and the farmer baled on the average 789 bales a day. How many bales would they bale in 6 days?

7. The Textile Shop teaches 372 students a year. If each one makes a dress that requires 5 m of material, how much material must be purchased at the beginning of each year?

1. 86 ×23	55 ×15	74 ×34	63 ×42	82 ×53	91 ×25
2. 86 ×43	75 ×45	43 ×32	85 ×96	69 ×87	87 ×78
3. 92 ×78	38 ×68	27 ×29	56 ×38	65 ×47	74 ×56
4. 136 ×23	762 ×23	671 ×32	580 ×54	849 ×25	908 ×43
5. 935 ×68	186 ×79	727 ×87	604 ×96	583 ×87	492 ×65
6. 1308 ×23	5693 ×45	4728 ×35	3601 ×42	8362 ×24	6304 ×45
7. 7863 ×89	6094 ×97	2656 ×89	3784 ×78	2036 ×98	4216 ×86

Situation Solving

Work Here

1. Fred drives 53 km each day to get to and from work. How far does he drive in 20 days?

2. A hobby farmer's chickens lay on the average 89 eggs a day. How many eggs do they lay in a month of 31 days?

3. A case of peas holds 48 cans. How many cans will 32 cases hold?

4. A salesman travelled on the average 97 km a day while working in the city. How far would he travel in 1 work period of 26 days?

5. A handbill distributor hired 37 people to hand out 75 handbills each. How many handbills would be distributed?

6. A contractor hired 28 bricklayers for an apartment development. Each bricklayer could lay 83 bricks an hour. How many bricks would they lay in 1 h?

7. A light-bulb manufacturer packs 48 bulbs to a carton. How many bulbs will be packed in 65 cartons?

Situation Solving

1. Mr. Jones's orchard packed 276 cases of peaches with 48 peaches per case. How many peaches were packed?

2. If a small commercial airplane flies at 560 km/h, how far will the plane travel in 43 flying hours?

3. A travelling salesman travels on the average 1368 km every week. How far will he travel in 43 weeks?

4. One hundred forty-seven cases of food were sent to the flood relief fund. Each case held 83 meals. How many meals could be served?

5. Eastvale Vocational played 24 football games, and at each game there were 1768 paying visitors. What was the total attendance at the 24 games?

6. Each room in a motel is tiled with 1028 tiles. How much tile is required for 23 rooms?

7. A car manufacturer can produce 3360 cars a week. How many cars can be produced in a working year of 45 weeks?

Multiplying — dollars:

1.
| $1.26 | $4.37 | $5.96 | $2.65 | $3.24 | $3.16 |
| ×2 | ×4 | ×6 | ×7 | ×4 | ×6 |

2.
| $4.36 | $7.95 | $3.08 | $5.95 | $2.65 | $4.38 |
| ×9 | ×8 | ×6 | ×7 | ×5 | ×6 |

3.
| $17.29 | $18.56 | $39.72 | $45.26 | $58.63 | $92.89 |
| ×8 | ×6 | ×5 | ×8 | ×7 | ×9 |

4.
| $5.06 | $4.98 | $3.29 | $5.85 | $6.54 | $8.36 |
| ×26 | ×38 | ×93 | ×87 | ×68 | ×39 |

5.
| $0.06 | $4.90 | $40.04 | $4.80 | $6.58 | $3.86 |
| ×58 | ×89 | ×76 | ×39 | ×47 | ×72 |

6.
| $2.95 | $60.06 | $70.50 | $31.29 | $87.89 | $26.89 |
| ×86 | ×95 | ×72 | ×46 | ×38 | ×59 |

Situation Solving

1. Pearl bought 2 lipsticks at $1.40 each. How much did she pay?

2. Find the cost of 3 cans of juice at 59¢ a can.

3. Chris bought 7 model kits at $1.98 each. How much did they cost?

4. Dresses in the Sewing Shop sold for $15.95. How much would the shop take in if 9 dresses were sold?

5. Gary's parents rented a house for $415.00 a month. How much did they pay for one year's rent?

6. The cafeteria sold hot meals for $1.25. How much did they take in if they sold 113 meals?

7. A pair of snow tires sells for $59.95 in the Motor Service Shop. During November they sold 29 pairs of tires. What was the total received from the sale of the tires?

Situation Solving

8. The Horticulture Shop planted 23 rows of tulips. Each row contained 10 tulips and each tulip cost 35¢. Find the cost of planting the tulips.

9. Joe works part time in a restaurant. He worked 4 days the first week, 3 days the second week, 5 days the third week and 6 days the fourth week. How much did he earn if he made $18.50 a day?

10. North Vocational School held open house. They sold 325 adult tickets at 75¢ each and 176 student tickets at 50¢ each. How much money was collected from the sale of the tickets?

11. Bill bought 8 L of red paint at $3.60 a litre and 3 L of white paint at $4.09 a litre. What was the total cost of the paint?

12. The bus fare to Niagara Falls is $8.50 a person return. The train fare is $9.50 a person return. How much would a class of 23 pupils save by taking the bus?

13. A farmer sold 14 head of cattle for $383.00 each, and 19 pigs for $176.34 each. How much did he make from the sale of his livestock?

Division

Division by one number with no remainder:

1. $2\overline{)10}$ $2\overline{)18}$ $2\overline{)2}$ $2\overline{)6}$ $2\overline{)14}$ $2\overline{)8}$

    $2\overline{)4}$ $2\overline{)12}$ $2\overline{)16}$

2. $3\overline{)3}$ $3\overline{)24}$ $3\overline{)12}$ $3\overline{)18}$ $3\overline{)15}$ $3\overline{)6}$

    $3\overline{)27}$ $3\overline{)9}$ $3\overline{)21}$

3. $4\overline{)16}$ $4\overline{)28}$ $4\overline{)8}$ $4\overline{)32}$ $4\overline{)4}$ $4\overline{)24}$

    $4\overline{)12}$ $4\overline{)20}$ $4\overline{)36}$

4. $5\overline{)45}$ $5\overline{)20}$ $5\overline{)5}$ $5\overline{)30}$ $5\overline{)15}$ $5\overline{)40}$

    $5\overline{)25}$ $5\overline{)10}$ $5\overline{)35}$

5. $6\overline{)54}$ $6\overline{)30}$ $6\overline{)18}$ $6\overline{)42}$ $6\overline{)24}$ $6\overline{)48}$

    $6\overline{)12}$ $6\overline{)36}$ $6\overline{)6}$

6. $7\overline{)7}$ $7\overline{)35}$ $7\overline{)56}$ $7\overline{)14}$ $7\overline{)63}$ $7\overline{)21}$

    $7\overline{)49}$ $7\overline{)28}$ $7\overline{)42}$

7. $8\overline{)48}$ $8\overline{)16}$ $8\overline{)72}$ $8\overline{)40}$ $8\overline{)24}$ $8\overline{)64}$

    $8\overline{)32}$ $8\overline{)8}$ $8\overline{)56}$

8. $9\overline{)36}$ $9\overline{)9}$ $9\overline{)81}$ $9\overline{)63}$ $9\overline{)27}$ $9\overline{)54}$

    $9\overline{)45}$ $9\overline{)72}$ $9\overline{)18}$

Situation Solving

1. Andy delivered 54 book orders in 6 days. What was the average number of deliveries a day?

2. Nine boys sold 36 magazines. How many did each boy sell, if they all sold the same number of copies?

3. Each of 5 girls made a gun rack in the woodworking shop. They used a total of 45 m of lumber. How much lumber did each girl use?

4. There were 56 windows to clean. The 7 boys who did the job each cleaned the same number. How many windows did each boy clean?

5. The class nominated 8 boys to collect baskets for the Basket Drive. They collected 72 baskets. How many did each boy collect?

6. Eight people made 40 garments in Dry Cleaning. How many garments did each person make?

7. Six Home Economics students had to make 42 pies for a party. How many pies did each student make?

43

Situation Solving

Work Here

1. Six students from the Horticulture Shop planted 72 evergreen trees. How many trees did each student plant?

2. The Mass Production Shop packaged 216 articles in 9 boxes. How many articles were in each box?

3. The 3 boys on the Social Committee sold 465 tickets for the School Social. How many tickets did each boy sell?

4. Trowel Trades produced 780 patio slabs to be used on 6 patios. How many slabs were used to construct each patio?

5. Paul drove 1336 km in 8 days of his holiday. How many kilometres did he drive each day?

6. The cafeteria sold 3865 L of milk in 5 days. How many litres of milk were sold each day?

7. In one week 9688 handbills were delivered by 7 people. How many did each person deliver in the week?

1. $2\overline{)24}$ $4\overline{)48}$ $2\overline{)36}$ $3\overline{)96}$ $5\overline{)65}$

2. $6\overline{)48}$ $5\overline{)45}$ $2\overline{)24}$ $6\overline{)54}$ $5\overline{)25}$

3. $4\overline{)372}$ $4\overline{)292}$ $5\overline{)460}$ $6\overline{)318}$ $3\overline{)285}$

4. $2\overline{)216}$ $4\overline{)496}$ $3\overline{)645}$ $6\overline{)258}$ $4\overline{)964}$

5. $6\overline{)864}$ $4\overline{)504}$ $5\overline{)265}$ $6\overline{)936}$ $4\overline{)5484}$

Division with remainders:

A number may not always divide evenly into another number. When a number less than the divisor is left over after you have calculated the problem, it is called a remainder. Here are two common methods of showing the remainder:

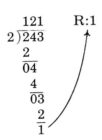
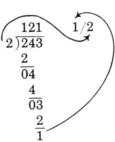

Solve these problems:

1. $6\overline{)1642}$ $2\overline{)1163}$ $3\overline{)8326}$ $2\overline{)9459}$ $6\overline{)2789}$

2. $3\overline{)6451}$ $2\overline{)4933}$ $5\overline{)6046}$ $6\overline{)2416}$ $4\overline{)9262}$

45

1. $7\overline{)49}$ $9\overline{)81}$ $8\overline{)64}$ $7\overline{)56}$ $8\overline{)32}$

2. $9\overline{)63}$ $8\overline{)72}$ $7\overline{)42}$ $9\overline{)45}$ $8\overline{)48}$

3. $9\overline{)819}$ $7\overline{)651}$ $8\overline{)496}$ $9\overline{)756}$ $7\overline{)595}$

4. $8\overline{)876}$ $7\overline{)489}$ $8\overline{)376}$ $8\overline{)486}$ $7\overline{)374}$

5. $9\overline{)786}$ $8\overline{)498}$ $7\overline{)976}$ $9\overline{)834}$ $8\overline{)987}$

6. $7\overline{)9421}$ $8\overline{)3787}$ $8\overline{)7969}$ $9\overline{)2393}$ $7\overline{)4896}$

7. $9\overline{)3876}$ $8\overline{)3789}$ $7\overline{)7864}$ $9\overline{)3894}$ $8\overline{)7869}$

1. $41\overline{)820}$ $11\overline{)385}$ $21\overline{)651}$ $31\overline{)992}$ $12\overline{)660}$

2. $41\overline{)902}$ $31\overline{)744}$ $13\overline{)273}$ $11\overline{)231}$ $12\overline{)492}$

3. $42\overline{)3452}$ $32\overline{)1383}$ $32\overline{)7534}$ $43\overline{)9163}$ $72\overline{)3754}$

4. $63\overline{)4892}$ $81\overline{)3895}$ $76\overline{)9876}$ $93\overline{)8954}$ $79\overline{)7036}$

5. $97\overline{)9084}$ $63\overline{)9486}$ $88\overline{)8907}$ $80\overline{)8609}$ $49\overline{)3096}$

6. $78\overline{)7348}$ $87\overline{)9304}$ $76\overline{)8943}$ $62\overline{)3489}$ $26\overline{)4020}$

Situation Solving

1. The cafeteria made 92 sandwiches for their 23 guests. How many sandwiches were made for each?

2. A class of 35 students read 280 books during the year. What is the average number of books read by each student?

3. A grocer had 5780 kg of potatoes. If he put 90 kg of potatoes in a sack, how many sacks would he fill?

4. If 32 books are packed in a carton, how many cartons can be filled with 1824 books?

5. A dump truck carries 1500 kg of sand. How many trips would be needed to deliver 34 500 kg of sand?

6. Mr. Jones drove 1058 km. If he used 46 L of gasoline, how many kilometres did he get to each litre?

7. A local store hired 68 people to deliver 12 396 catalogues. How many catalogues did each person deliver?

Division — dollars:

1. $2\overline{)\$0.46}$ $8\overline{)\$0.64}$ $5\overline{)\$0.55}$ $7\overline{)\$0.56}$ $9\overline{)\$0.72}$

2. $9\overline{)\$1.89}$ $7\overline{)\$39.27}$ $3\overline{)\$14.95}$ $5\overline{)\$94.50}$ $4\overline{)\$15.12}$

3. $7\overline{)\$16.33}$ $9\overline{)\$47.88}$ $6\overline{)\$34.91}$ $5\overline{)\$51.43}$ $8\overline{)\$74.89}$

4. $21\overline{)\$18.90}$ $46\overline{)\$8.28}$ $73\overline{)\$29.93}$ $83\overline{)\$17.43}$ $67\overline{)\$32.16}$

5. $63\overline{)\$21.97}$ $41\overline{)\$63.84}$ $93\overline{)\$763.91}$ $74\overline{)\$88.03}$ $16\overline{)\$74.96}$

6. $71\overline{)\$40.88}$ $80\overline{)\$790.99}$ $34\overline{)\$74.08}$ $96\overline{)\$26.96}$ $76\overline{)\$83.67}$

7. $23\overline{)\$29.63}$ $95\overline{)\$89.50}$ $86\overline{)\$24.95}$ $67\overline{)\$865.50}$ $36\overline{)\$9605.86}$

Situation Solving

1. How many 17-cent stamps can Betty buy with $1.53?

2. Eight girls shared the cost of a party. Total cost was $28.00. How much did each girl pay as her share?

3. Bill earned $80.00 for 5 days' work doing odd jobs. How much did he make a day?

4. Mrs. Smith bought 21 m of material at $73.50. How much did 1 m cost?

5. For 1 year the total household expenses were $3640.00. What was the average expense per week? (Hint: There are 52 weeks in one year.)

6. Mary got a job as a cab driver. She earned $10 320.00 a year. How much did she make in three months? (Hint: There are 12 months in one year.)

7. Eastern Public Library bought 580 books for $4060.00. What was the average cost per book?

8. The Woodworking Shop bought $290.40 worth of pine. This material was to be used by 34 pupils. What is the cost of each pupil's share of the wood?

9. John made $35.20 delivering telephone books. If he delivered 1760 books, how much did he get for each one?

10. Mrs. Valenti spent $46.00 in 20 days for gasoline. It costs $0.26 per litre. She drove 2300 km.

    (a) How many litres of gasoline did she buy? _____

    (b) How many kilometres did she get per litre? _____

    (c) How many litres of gasoline did she use a day? _____

11. A dealer bought 18 refrigerators for $6400.00. For how much must he sell each refrigerator if he is to make $75.00 profit on each one?

12. Anna bought a car for $4400 with a down payment of $700. She financed it for a period of 36 months. How much will her monthly payment be?

13. The Lamberts bought a refrigerator for $736.00, a stove for $587.00 and small appliances for $245.00. The sales tax was $109.76 and the financing service charge was $352.00. If the items are repaid in 36 months, how much will the monthly payments be?

CHAPTER TWO
COMMON FRACTIONS

Numerator and Denominator

Parts of a proper fraction:

$$\frac{1}{2}$$

⟶ Numerator—tells the part of the whole.

⟶ Denominator—tells the number of parts into which the whole has been divided.

Remember: When adding fractions with like denominators, add the numerators only.

3. Add the following:

(a) $\dfrac{1}{4} + \dfrac{2}{4} =$ (b) $\dfrac{1}{5} + \dfrac{1}{5} =$ (c) $\dfrac{1}{6} + \dfrac{2}{6} =$

(d) $\dfrac{1}{7} + \dfrac{1}{7} =$ (e) $\dfrac{1}{8} + \dfrac{4}{8} =$ (f) $\dfrac{1}{5} + \dfrac{2}{5} =$

(g) $\dfrac{3}{7} + \dfrac{3}{7} =$ (h) $\dfrac{3}{6} + \dfrac{2}{6} =$ (i) $\dfrac{1}{7} + \dfrac{2}{7} =$

(j) $\dfrac{5}{8} + \dfrac{2}{8} =$ (k) $\dfrac{2}{7} + \dfrac{3}{7} =$ (l) $\dfrac{1}{8} + \dfrac{2}{8} =$

(m) $\dfrac{3}{8} + \dfrac{4}{8} =$ (n) $\dfrac{1}{9} + \dfrac{4}{9} =$ (o) $\dfrac{1}{10} + \dfrac{2}{10} =$

(p) $\dfrac{1}{12} + \dfrac{6}{12} =$ (q) $\dfrac{4}{13} + \dfrac{1}{13} =$ (r) $\dfrac{3}{24} + \dfrac{2}{24} =$

4. Add:

(a) $\dfrac{1}{8}$ $+\dfrac{2}{8}$ (a) $\dfrac{1}{4}$ $+\dfrac{2}{4}$ (c) $\dfrac{3}{6}$ $+\dfrac{2}{6}$ (d) $\dfrac{1}{7}$ $+\dfrac{4}{7}$

(e) $\dfrac{1}{7}$ $\dfrac{5}{+7}$ (f) $\dfrac{6}{9}$ $\dfrac{1}{+9}$ (g) $\dfrac{3}{8}$ $\dfrac{4}{+8}$ (h) $\dfrac{9}{12}$ $\dfrac{2}{+12}$

(i) $\dfrac{3}{8}$ $+\dfrac{2}{8}$ (j) $\dfrac{7}{14}$ $+\dfrac{2}{14}$ (k) $\dfrac{5}{9}$ $+\dfrac{2}{9}$ (l) $\dfrac{3}{12}$ $+\dfrac{2}{12}$

Reducing Fractions

Reducing to lowest terms:

A fraction may be written in several ways and still represent the same amount of the whole. Study the example below and answer the questions.

A   B

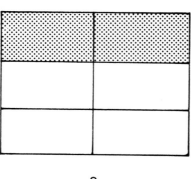   =   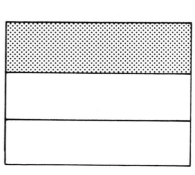

$$\frac{2}{6} \qquad = \qquad \frac{1}{3}$$

1. How does Figure A compare in size to Figure B?_____

2. Figure A is divided into how many parts?_____

3. Figure B is divided into how many parts?_____

4. What fraction of Figure A is shaded?_____

5. What fraction of Figure B is shaded?_____

6. How does the shaded part of Figure A compare in size to the shaded part in Figure B?_____

_____

7. How do the fractions $\frac{2}{6}$ and $\frac{1}{3}$ compare in size?_____

$\frac{2}{6}$ can be reduced to $\frac{1}{3}$.

For an easy way to reduce fractions study the example below.

$$\frac{2}{6} = \left(\frac{2 \div 2}{6 \div 2}\right) = \frac{1}{3}$$

Rule: To reduce fractions divide the numerator and the denominator by the same number.

Reduce:

1. $\frac{4}{6} =$ 2. $\frac{8}{10} =$ 3. $\frac{2}{6} =$ 4. $\frac{6}{8} =$ 5. $\frac{6}{10} =$

6. $\frac{3}{9} =$ 7. $\frac{6}{9} =$ 8. $\frac{3}{6} =$ 9. $\frac{9}{12} =$ 10. $\frac{12}{15} =$

11. $\frac{4}{12} =$ 12. $\frac{12}{16} =$ 13. $\frac{8}{20} =$ 14. $\frac{4}{16} =$ 15. $\frac{4}{32} =$

16. $\frac{9}{15} =$ 17. $\frac{3}{12} =$ 18. $\frac{8}{12} =$ 19. $\frac{12}{24} =$ 20. $\frac{4}{20} =$

21. $\frac{2}{4} =$ 22. $\frac{6}{10} =$ 23. $\frac{4}{14} =$ 24. $\frac{2}{12} =$ 25. $\frac{3}{15} =$

26. $\frac{4}{18} =$ 27. $\frac{8}{14} =$ 28. $\frac{6}{15} =$ 29. $\frac{4}{10} =$ 30. $\frac{10}{15} =$

31. $\frac{12}{18} =$ 32. $\frac{7}{14} =$ 33. $\frac{5}{10} =$ 34. $\frac{14}{18} =$ 35. $\frac{10}{12} =$

Watch for this:

A. $\frac{3}{3} = \left(\frac{3 \div 3}{3 \div 3}\right) = \frac{1}{1} = 1$

B. $\frac{7}{7} = \left(\frac{7 \div 7}{7 \div 7}\right) = \frac{1}{1} = 1$

C. $\frac{15}{15} = \left(\frac{15 \div 15}{15 \div 15}\right) = \frac{1}{1} = 1$

> If the numerator is the same as the denominator the value of the fraction is one whole.

---

36. $\frac{5}{15} =$ 37. $\frac{2}{2} =$ 38. $\frac{90}{100} =$ 39. $\frac{2}{8} =$ 40. $\frac{6}{16} =$

41. $\frac{3}{12} =$ 42. $\frac{8}{56} =$ 43. $\frac{6}{18} =$ 44. $\frac{5}{5} =$ 45. $\frac{8}{16} =$

46. $\frac{4}{4} =$ 47. $\frac{6}{14} =$ 48. $\frac{18}{24} =$ 49. $\frac{10}{14} =$ 50. $\frac{3}{6} =$

51. $\frac{2}{18} =$ 52. $\frac{12}{12} =$ 53. $\frac{9}{18} =$ 54. $\frac{4}{8} =$ 55. $\frac{12}{16} =$

56. $\frac{10}{10} =$ 57. $\frac{2}{10} =$ 58. $\frac{12}{15} =$ 59. $\frac{9}{9} =$ 60. $\frac{14}{16} =$

61. $\frac{10}{18} =$ 62. $\frac{6}{6} =$ 63. $\frac{36}{40} =$ 64. $\frac{12}{14} =$ 65. $\frac{6}{12} =$

66. $\frac{8}{18} =$ 67. $\frac{2}{14} =$ 68. $\frac{40}{60} =$ 69. $\frac{2}{16} =$ 70. $\frac{12}{12} =$

Addition of like fractions with reducing:

Study the example and calculate the questions below.

$$\frac{2}{6} + \frac{2}{6} = \frac{4}{6}\left(\frac{4 \div 2}{6 \div 2}\right) = \frac{2}{3}$$

or

$$\frac{1}{3} + \frac{2}{3} = \frac{3}{3}\left(\frac{3 \div 3}{3 \div 3}\right) = \frac{1}{1} = 1$$

1. $\frac{1}{4} + \frac{1}{4} =$

2. $\frac{2}{6} + \frac{2}{6} =$

3. $\frac{3}{4} + \frac{1}{4} =$

4. $\frac{3}{8} + \frac{1}{8} =$

5. $\frac{1}{6} + \frac{1}{6} =$

6. $\frac{1}{8} + \frac{1}{8} =$

7. $\frac{1}{9} + \frac{2}{9} =$

8. $\frac{3}{8} + \frac{3}{8} =$

9. $\frac{4}{5} + \frac{1}{5} =$

10. $\frac{3}{7} + \frac{4}{7} =$

11. $\frac{2}{9} + \frac{1}{9} =$

12. $\frac{3}{9} + \frac{3}{9} =$

13. $\frac{2}{10} + \frac{3}{10} =$

14. $\frac{3}{10} + \frac{5}{10} =$

15. $\frac{7}{9} + \frac{2}{9} =$

16. $\frac{3}{12} + \frac{3}{12} =$

17. $\frac{6}{12} + \frac{3}{12} =$

18. $\frac{4}{10} + \frac{4}{10} =$

19. $\frac{3}{6}$
$+\frac{1}{6}$

20. $\frac{1}{9}$
$+\frac{8}{9}$

21. $\frac{1}{12}$
$+\frac{3}{12}$

22. $\frac{9}{12}$
$+\frac{3}{12}$

23. $\frac{4}{8}$
$+\frac{2}{8}$

24. $\frac{1}{16}$
$+\frac{3}{16}$

25. $\frac{15}{16}$
$+\frac{1}{16}$

26. $\frac{4}{5}$
$+\frac{1}{5}$

27. $\frac{4}{10}$
$+\frac{2}{10}$

28. $\frac{7}{14}$
$+\frac{3}{14}$

29. $\frac{14}{32}$
$+\frac{16}{32}$

30. $\frac{4}{50}$
$+\frac{10}{50}$

31. $\frac{26}{100}$
$+\frac{30}{100}$

32. $\frac{24}{50}$
$+\frac{10}{50}$

33. $\frac{3}{16}$
$+\frac{5}{16}$

Improper Fractions and Mixed Numbers

Reducing improper fractions to mixed numbers:

$$\frac{4}{4} \qquad + \qquad \frac{1}{4} \qquad = \qquad \frac{5}{4}$$

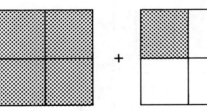

$$1 \text{ whole} \quad + \quad \frac{1}{4} \quad = \quad 1\frac{1}{4}$$

$\frac{5}{4}$ may be reduced to $1\frac{1}{4}$
    the mixed fraction

For an easy way to reduce improper fractions to mixed fractions, study the example below.

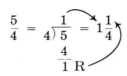

$$\frac{5}{4} = 4\overline{)5} = 1\frac{1}{4}$$

Rule: To reduce an improper fraction to a mixed fraction divide the denominator into the numerator.

Reduce the improper fractions to mixed numbers:

1. $\frac{3}{2} =$ 2. $\frac{4}{3} =$ 3. $\frac{7}{2} =$ 4. $\frac{9}{7} =$

5. $\frac{8}{3} =$ 6. $\frac{12}{5} =$ 7. $\frac{15}{7} =$ 8. $\frac{23}{4} =$

9. $\frac{19}{4} =$ 10. $\frac{36}{5} =$ 11. $\frac{41}{8} =$ 12. $\frac{18}{4} =$

13. $\frac{21}{4} =$ 14. $\frac{6}{5} =$ 15. $\frac{13}{6} =$ 16. $\frac{15}{8} =$

17. $\frac{7}{3} =$ 18. $\frac{9}{7} =$ 19. $\frac{12}{7} =$ 20. $\frac{9}{4} =$

21. $\frac{11}{7} =$

Watch for this:

$$\boxed{\frac{18}{4} = 4\frac{2}{4} \quad \text{reduce to } 4\frac{1}{2}}$$

22. $\frac{10}{4} =$ 23. $\frac{20}{6} =$ 24. $\frac{18}{4} =$ 25. $\frac{42}{8} =$

26. $\frac{44}{8} =$ 27. $\frac{40}{12} =$ 28. $\frac{30}{9} =$ 29. $\frac{26}{4} =$

30. $\frac{6}{4} =$ 31. $\frac{34}{4} =$ 32. $\frac{45}{10} =$ 33. $\frac{38}{8} =$

Addition of Fractions

Addition with reducing in the sum:

Study the example below and calculate the questions.

$$\frac{5}{6} + \frac{5}{6} = \frac{10}{6} = \left(6 \overline{)\begin{array}{l} 1 \\ 10 \\ \underline{6} \\ 4 \ R \end{array}} \right) = 1\frac{4}{6} = 1\frac{2}{3}$$

1. $\dfrac{3}{4} + \dfrac{3}{4} =$

2. $\dfrac{2}{3} + \dfrac{2}{3} =$

3. $\dfrac{4}{5} + \dfrac{2}{5} =$

4. $\dfrac{2}{6} + \dfrac{5}{6} =$

5. $\dfrac{4}{7} + \dfrac{4}{7} =$

6. $\dfrac{2}{8} + \dfrac{7}{8} =$

7. $\dfrac{3}{9} + \dfrac{7}{9} =$

8. $\dfrac{2}{3} + \dfrac{3}{3} =$

9. $\dfrac{3}{5} + \dfrac{3}{5} =$

10. $\dfrac{3}{10} + \dfrac{8}{10} =$

11. $\dfrac{4}{5} + \dfrac{3}{5} =$

12. $\dfrac{6}{9} + \dfrac{6}{9} =$

13. $\dfrac{9}{12} + \dfrac{6}{12} =$

14. $\dfrac{5}{7} + \dfrac{5}{7} =$

15. $\dfrac{3}{6} + \dfrac{4}{6} =$

16. $\dfrac{4}{5} + \dfrac{4}{5} =$

17. $\dfrac{7}{8} + \dfrac{7}{8} =$

18. $\dfrac{9}{10} + \dfrac{9}{10} =$

19. $\dfrac{6}{8} + \dfrac{4}{8} =$

20. $\dfrac{16}{24} + \dfrac{10}{24} =$

21. $\dfrac{8}{9} + \dfrac{8}{9} =$

22. $\dfrac{5}{7}$ $+\dfrac{4}{7}$

23. $\dfrac{17}{18}$ $+\dfrac{4}{18}$

24. $\dfrac{4}{6}$ $+\dfrac{4}{6}$

25. $\dfrac{9}{12}$ $+\dfrac{9}{12}$

26. $\dfrac{6}{7}$ $+\dfrac{6}{7}$

27. $\dfrac{7}{8}$ $+\dfrac{3}{8}$

28. $\dfrac{5}{6}$ $+\dfrac{4}{6}$

29. $\dfrac{23}{30}$ $+\dfrac{9}{30}$

30. $\dfrac{4}{50}$ $+\dfrac{49}{50}$

31. $\dfrac{5}{6}$ $+\dfrac{5}{6}$

32. $\dfrac{20}{32}$ $+\dfrac{23}{32}$

33. $\dfrac{7}{10}$ $+\dfrac{7}{10}$

34. $\dfrac{6}{7}$ $+\dfrac{5}{7}$

35. $\dfrac{24}{27}$ $+\dfrac{21}{27}$

36. $\dfrac{9}{23}$ $+\dfrac{21}{23}$

Addition of mixed numbers:

Study the example below and calculate the questions.

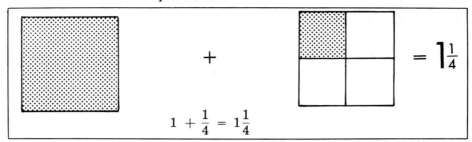

$$1 + \frac{1}{4} = 1\frac{1}{4}$$

1. $2 + \frac{1}{3} =$

2. $\frac{1}{8} + 4 =$

3. $\frac{3}{4} + 4 =$

4. $9 + \frac{1}{5} =$

5. $\frac{7}{8} + 2 =$

6. $6 + \frac{2}{3} =$

Study the example below and calculate the questions.

$$2 + 1\frac{1}{4} = 3\frac{1}{4}$$

7. $2 + 3\frac{2}{5} =$

8. $7\frac{7}{8} + 8 =$

9. $4 + 9\frac{9}{10} =$

10. $8\frac{4}{7} + 2 =$

11. $2 + 6\frac{2}{3} =$

12. $9 + 5\frac{4}{5} =$

Study the example below and calculate the questions.

$$2\frac{1}{3} + 2\frac{1}{3} = 4\frac{2}{3}$$

13. $2\frac{3}{7} + 4\frac{1}{7} =$

14. $9\frac{2}{5} + 4\frac{2}{5} =$

15. $6\frac{3}{10} + 1\frac{4}{10} =$

16. $2\frac{1}{4} + 3\frac{1}{4} =$

17. $6\frac{3}{10} + 2\frac{3}{10} =$

18. $4\frac{1}{8} + 2\frac{3}{8} =$

19. $3\frac{1}{4} + 3\frac{3}{4} =$

20. $4\frac{2}{5} + 3\frac{1}{5} =$

21. $2\frac{3}{8} + 3\frac{3}{8} =$

22. $6\frac{1}{4} + 1\frac{2}{4} =$

23. $4\frac{1}{5} + 3\frac{3}{5} =$

24. $8\frac{1}{8} + 4\frac{5}{8} =$

25. $9\frac{5}{8} + 6\frac{1}{8} =$

26. $7\frac{1}{12} + 2\frac{9}{12} =$

59

Study the example below and calculate the questions:

$$4\tfrac{3}{4}\qquad \left(6 + 1\tfrac{2}{4} = 7\tfrac{2}{4}\right)$$
$$+2\tfrac{3}{4}$$
$$\overline{6\tfrac{6}{4}}\qquad \left(\tfrac{6}{4} = 1\tfrac{2}{4}\right) = 7\tfrac{2}{4} = 7\tfrac{1}{2}$$

1. $\quad 4\tfrac{3}{5}$
$\quad +2\tfrac{4}{5}$

2. $\quad 8\tfrac{5}{6}$
$\quad +8\tfrac{5}{6}$

3. $\quad 4\tfrac{9}{10}$
$\quad +1\tfrac{3}{10}$

4. $\quad 7\tfrac{11}{12}$
$\quad +6\tfrac{5}{12}$

5. $\quad 3\tfrac{11}{15}$
$\quad +2\tfrac{9}{15}$

6. $\quad 8\tfrac{2}{3}$
$\quad +4\tfrac{2}{3}$

7. $\quad 6\tfrac{1}{2}$
$\quad +9\tfrac{1}{2}$

8. $\quad 3\tfrac{7}{8}$
$\quad +4\tfrac{2}{8}$

9. $\quad 7\tfrac{2}{7}$
$\quad +3\tfrac{6}{7}$

10. $\quad 9\tfrac{7}{8}$
$\quad +8\tfrac{5}{8}$

11. $\quad 7\tfrac{2}{3}$
$\quad +6\tfrac{2}{3}$

12. $\quad 3\tfrac{5}{10}$
$\quad +8\tfrac{9}{10}$

13. $\quad 4\tfrac{5}{6}$
$\quad +12\tfrac{2}{6}$

14. $\quad 6\tfrac{9}{10}$
$\quad +18\tfrac{3}{10}$

15. $\quad 10\tfrac{3}{8}$
$\quad +7\tfrac{7}{8}$

16. $\quad 6\tfrac{4}{6}$
$\quad +19\tfrac{3}{6}$

17. $\quad 14\tfrac{3}{16}$
$\quad +13\tfrac{14}{16}$

18. $\quad 16\tfrac{7}{8}$
$\quad +12\tfrac{7}{8}$

19. $\quad 17\tfrac{4}{5}$
$\quad +11\tfrac{2}{5}$

20. $\quad 21\tfrac{3}{8}$
$\quad +12\tfrac{7}{8}$

21. $\quad 16\tfrac{5}{10}$
$\quad +23\tfrac{9}{10}$

22. $\quad 32\tfrac{4}{5}$
$\quad +21\tfrac{3}{5}$

23. $\quad 24\tfrac{4}{6}$
$\quad +39\tfrac{5}{6}$

24. $\quad 61\tfrac{3}{9}$
$\quad +48\tfrac{8}{9}$

25. $\quad 16\tfrac{3}{5}$
$\quad +21\tfrac{4}{5}$

26. $\quad 46\tfrac{7}{12}$
$\quad +59\tfrac{8}{12}$

27. $\quad 92\tfrac{20}{23}$
$\quad +103\tfrac{13}{23}$

28. $\quad 46\tfrac{45}{56}$
$\quad +27\tfrac{20}{56}$

Add (be sure to change the improper fractions to mixed numbers):

1. $2\frac{2}{3} + 3\frac{2}{3} =$

2. $9\frac{4}{7} + 6\frac{6}{7} =$

3. $5\frac{3}{4} + 6\frac{3}{4} =$

4. $9\frac{2}{5} + 6\frac{4}{5} =$

5. $14\frac{9}{10} + 9\frac{7}{10} =$

6. $4\frac{3}{5} + 6\frac{3}{5} =$

7. $12\frac{7}{10} + 3\frac{6}{10} =$

8. $8\frac{4}{5} + 3\frac{4}{5} =$

9. $24\frac{5}{9} + 6\frac{3}{9} =$

10. $4\frac{11}{12} + 6\frac{10}{12} =$

11. $43\frac{7}{8} + \frac{6}{8} =$

12. $4\frac{1}{9} + 6\frac{8}{9} =$

13. $5\frac{6}{7}$
    $+2\frac{5}{7}$
    $\overline{}$

14. $9\frac{4}{6}$
    $+2\frac{3}{6}$
    $\overline{}$

15. $21\frac{5}{8}$
    $+4\frac{6}{8}$
    $\overline{}$

16. $9\frac{5}{10}$
    $+7\frac{6}{10}$
    $\overline{}$

17. $204\frac{3}{16}$
    $+31\frac{12}{16}$
    $\overline{}$

18. $6\frac{3}{5}$
    $+9\frac{4}{5}$
    $\overline{}$

19. $8\frac{7}{8}$
    $+6\frac{6}{8}$
    $\overline{}$

20. $4\frac{9}{12}$
    $+7\frac{4}{12}$
    $\overline{}$

21. $21\frac{9}{16}$
    $+30\frac{9}{16}$
    $\overline{}$

22. $16\frac{16}{21}$
    $+23\frac{20}{21}$
    $\overline{}$

23. $14\frac{14}{30}$
    $+83\frac{20}{30}$
    $\overline{}$

24. $21\frac{32}{50}$
    $+56\frac{34}{50}$
    $\overline{}$

25. $63\frac{16}{33}$
    $+47\frac{24}{33}$
    $\overline{}$

26. $83\frac{36}{60}$
    $+56\frac{29}{60}$
    $\overline{}$

27. $62\frac{40}{45}$
    $+72\frac{30}{45}$
    $\overline{}$

Common denominators:

Sam was making cake and muffins. He needed ½ L of sugar for the cake and ¼ L of sugar for the muffins. How much sugar did he need?

A   B

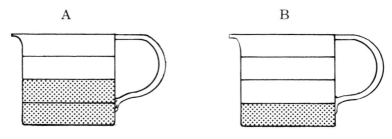

1. Figure A represents how much sugar?_____

2. Figure B represents how much sugar?_____

3. Are the denominators in each fraction the same?_____

Before adding fractions with unlike denominators, a common denominator must be found.

$$\frac{1}{2} = \left(\frac{1 \times 2}{2 \times 2} = \frac{2}{4}\right) \frac{2}{4} \qquad \frac{1}{2} + \frac{1}{4} = \frac{2}{4} + \frac{1}{4} = \frac{3}{4}$$

$$+ \frac{1}{4} = \qquad\qquad \frac{1}{4} \quad \text{or}$$

$$\overline{} \qquad \frac{3}{4} \qquad \left(\frac{1 \times 2}{2 \times 2} = \frac{2}{4}\right)$$

---

1. Why is ½ the same as 2/4 ?_____

2. What is the common denominator in the question above? _____

3. Find the common denominator for the following groups of fractions.

(a) $\frac{1}{2}$ and $\frac{1}{6}$ denominator_____   (b) $\frac{1}{4}$ and $\frac{1}{12}$ denominator_____

(c) $\frac{1}{5}$ and $\frac{1}{15}$ denominator_____   (d) $\frac{1}{3}$ and $\frac{1}{9}$ denominator_____

(e) $\frac{1}{2}$ and $\frac{1}{10}$ denominator_____   (f) $\frac{1}{6}$ and $\frac{1}{12}$ denominator_____

(g) $\frac{1}{4}$ and $\frac{1}{8}$ denominator_____   (h) $\frac{1}{5}$ and $\frac{1}{10}$ denominator_____

(i) $\frac{1}{3}$ and $\frac{1}{6}$ denominator_____   (j) $\frac{1}{4}$ and $\frac{1}{16}$ denominator_____

Addition of fractions with unlike denominators:

Add the following fractions:

1. $\dfrac{2}{3} + \dfrac{1}{6} =$ 2. $\dfrac{4}{10} + \dfrac{1}{5} =$ 3. $\dfrac{1}{12} + \dfrac{1}{6} =$

4. $\dfrac{1}{4} + \dfrac{3}{8} =$ 5. $\dfrac{1}{6} + \dfrac{3}{18} =$ 6. $\dfrac{2}{5} + \dfrac{1}{10} =$

7. $\begin{aligned}&\dfrac{1}{3}\\+&\dfrac{2}{9}\\\hline\end{aligned}$ 8. $\begin{aligned}&\dfrac{2}{3}\\+&\dfrac{1}{12}\\\hline\end{aligned}$ 9. $\begin{aligned}&\dfrac{4}{9}\\+&\dfrac{1}{3}\\\hline\end{aligned}$ 10. $\begin{aligned}&\dfrac{1}{4}\\+&\dfrac{3}{8}\\\hline\end{aligned}$ 11. $\begin{aligned}&\dfrac{1}{4}\\+&\dfrac{3}{16}\\\hline\end{aligned}$ 12. $\begin{aligned}&\dfrac{1}{2}\\+&\dfrac{3}{10}\\\hline\end{aligned}$

Study the example below and calculate the following:

$$
\begin{aligned}
1\tfrac{2}{3} &= 1\tfrac{4}{6} \qquad \text{or} \qquad 1\tfrac{2}{3} + 4\tfrac{5}{6} = 1\tfrac{4}{6} + 4\tfrac{5}{6} = 5\left(\tfrac{9}{6} = 1\tfrac{3}{6} = 1\tfrac{1}{2}\right) = 6\tfrac{1}{2}\\
4\tfrac{5}{6} &= 4\tfrac{5}{6}\\
\hline
5\tfrac{9}{6} &= 5\left(\tfrac{9}{6} = 1\tfrac{3}{6} = 1\tfrac{1}{2}\right) = 6\tfrac{1}{2}
\end{aligned}
$$

13. $\begin{aligned}&2\tfrac{1}{3}\\+&3\tfrac{5}{6}\\\hline\end{aligned}$ 14. $\begin{aligned}&4\tfrac{3}{4}\\+&6\tfrac{1}{2}\\\hline\end{aligned}$ 15. $\begin{aligned}&9\tfrac{7}{8}\\+&10\tfrac{3}{4}\\\hline\end{aligned}$ 16. $\begin{aligned}&4\tfrac{7}{10}\\+&9\tfrac{2}{5}\\\hline\end{aligned}$ 17. $\begin{aligned}&8\tfrac{2}{3}\\+&7\tfrac{1}{6}\\\hline\end{aligned}$

18. $\begin{aligned}&4\tfrac{6}{7}\\+&3\tfrac{3}{21}\\\hline\end{aligned}$ 19. $\begin{aligned}&6\tfrac{5}{6}\\+&2\tfrac{1}{12}\\\hline\end{aligned}$ 20. $\begin{aligned}&7\tfrac{4}{5}\\+&8\tfrac{3}{10}\\\hline\end{aligned}$ 21. $\begin{aligned}&9\tfrac{3}{4}\\+&3\tfrac{3}{12}\\\hline\end{aligned}$ 22. $\begin{aligned}&8\tfrac{1}{2}\\+&7\tfrac{7}{10}\\\hline\end{aligned}$

23. $6\tfrac{2}{5} + 7\tfrac{14}{15} =$ 24. $3\tfrac{1}{3} + 6\tfrac{7}{9} =$

25. $9\tfrac{1}{2} + 4\tfrac{5}{6} =$ 26. $9\tfrac{3}{5} + 6\tfrac{2}{10} =$

27. $7\tfrac{9}{10} + 3\tfrac{4}{5} =$ 28. $12\tfrac{3}{8} + 6\tfrac{1}{16} =$

29. $3\tfrac{4}{5} + 4\tfrac{2}{15} =$ 30. $8\tfrac{7}{8} + 2\tfrac{2}{24} =$

31. $3\tfrac{4}{9} + 12\tfrac{1}{27} =$ 32. $6\tfrac{2}{9} + 8\tfrac{4}{27} =$

Finding the common denominator by multiplying:

Step 1: Multiply the denominators to find the common denominator.

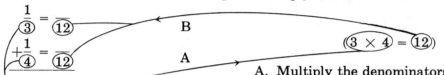

A. Multiply the denominators.
B. Use the product as the common denominator.

Step 2: Multiply the numerator by the same number as its denominator was multiplied by.

A: $\dfrac{1}{3}$ $\overset{\times 4}{=}$ $\dfrac{4}{12}$

B: $\dfrac{1}{4}$ $\overset{\times 3}{=}$ $\dfrac{3}{12}$

A. The denominator 3 was multiplied by 4 to find the common denominator of 12. Since the denominator was multiplied by 4, the numerator must also be multiplied by 4.

B. The denominator 4 was multiplied by 3 to find the common denominator of 12. Since the denominator was multiplied by 3, the numerator must also be multiplied by 3.

Therefore:

$$\dfrac{1}{3} = \dfrac{4}{12}$$
$$+\dfrac{1}{4} = \dfrac{3}{12}$$
$$\dfrac{7}{12}$$

1. In this question, write in the correct common denominator only.

$$\dfrac{4}{5} = \underline{\qquad}$$
$$\dfrac{2}{3} = \underline{\qquad}$$

2. Place the correct numerators in the question below.

$$\dfrac{4}{5} = \dfrac{}{15}$$
$$\dfrac{2}{3} = \dfrac{}{15}$$

3. Add: $\dfrac{4}{5} = \dfrac{12}{15}$

$$\dfrac{2}{3} = \dfrac{10}{15}$$

4. Reduce the answer: $\dfrac{4}{5} = \dfrac{12}{15}$

$$\dfrac{2}{3} = \dfrac{10}{15}$$

$$\dfrac{22}{15} =$$

If your work is correct, the answer will be $1\frac{7}{15}$.

5. Add the following fractions:

(1) $\frac{1}{2} + \frac{1}{3} =$ (2) $\frac{1}{2} + \frac{7}{9} =$

(3) $\frac{3}{5} + \frac{7}{12} =$ (4) $\frac{2}{3} + \frac{3}{4} =$

(5) $\frac{6}{7} + \frac{1}{4} =$ (6) $\frac{3}{4} + \frac{5}{7} =$

(7) $\frac{2}{3} + \frac{3}{10} =$ (8) $\frac{2}{5} + \frac{3}{8} =$

(9) $\frac{3}{7} + \frac{2}{3} =$ (10) $\frac{1}{9} + \frac{5}{8} =$

(11) $\frac{4}{5} + \frac{2}{3} =$ (12) $\frac{2}{7} + \frac{1}{2} =$

(13) $\begin{array}{r} \frac{2}{3} \\ +\frac{1}{5} \\ \hline \end{array}$ (14) $\begin{array}{r} \frac{6}{8} \\ +\frac{1}{3} \\ \hline \end{array}$ (15) $\begin{array}{r} \frac{4}{5} \\ +\frac{1}{2} \\ \hline \end{array}$ (16) $\begin{array}{r} \frac{1}{3} \\ +\frac{7}{8} \\ \hline \end{array}$

(17) $\begin{array}{r} \frac{3}{4} \\ +\frac{1}{3} \\ \hline \end{array}$ (18) $\begin{array}{r} \frac{9}{10} \\ +\frac{2}{5} \\ \hline \end{array}$ (19) $\begin{array}{r} \frac{7}{8} \\ +\frac{1}{2} \\ \hline \end{array}$ (20) $\begin{array}{r} \frac{3}{7} \\ +\frac{2}{5} \\ \hline \end{array}$

(21) $\begin{array}{r} \frac{1}{5} \\ +\frac{2}{3} \\ \hline \end{array}$ (22) $\begin{array}{r} \frac{1}{5} \\ +\frac{3}{8} \\ \hline \end{array}$ (23) $\begin{array}{r} \frac{6}{9} \\ +\frac{4}{5} \\ \hline \end{array}$ (24) $\begin{array}{r} \frac{2}{7} \\ +\frac{4}{5} \\ \hline \end{array}$

(25) $\begin{array}{r} \frac{2}{3} \\ +\frac{5}{7} \\ \hline \end{array}$ (26) $\begin{array}{r} \frac{7}{8} \\ +\frac{3}{5} \\ \hline \end{array}$ (27) $\begin{array}{r} \frac{1}{12} \\ +\frac{3}{20} \\ \hline \end{array}$ (28) $\begin{array}{r} \frac{2}{9} \\ +\frac{6}{8} \\ \hline \end{array}$

Study the example and do the questions.

$$\begin{aligned} 3\frac{2}{3} &= 3\frac{10}{15} \\ +2\frac{2}{5} &= 2\frac{6}{15} \\ \hline 5\frac{16}{15} &= 6\frac{1}{15} \end{aligned}$$

1. $7\frac{1}{2}$
$+3\frac{2}{3}$

2. $5\frac{5}{6}$
$+2\frac{3}{8}$

3. $2\frac{1}{5}$
$+3\frac{1}{3}$

4. $3\frac{1}{4}$
$+6\frac{8}{9}$

5. $3\frac{3}{5}$
$+2\frac{5}{6}$

6. $3\frac{4}{9}$
$+7\frac{1}{2}$

7. $6\frac{3}{5}$
$+2\frac{1}{4}$

8. $6\frac{2}{3}$
$+4\frac{3}{10}$

9. $8\frac{1}{3}$
$+4\frac{7}{11}$

10. $5\frac{4}{5}$
$+2\frac{5}{8}$

11. $6\frac{11}{12}$
$+5\frac{1}{5}$

12. $2\frac{5}{7}$
$+3\frac{1}{10}$

13. $6\frac{1}{8}$
$+3\frac{4}{5}$

14. $5\frac{3}{8}$
$+7\frac{7}{12}$

15. $7\frac{2}{3}$
$+5\frac{3}{7}$

16. $2\frac{1}{2}$
$+6\frac{3}{5}$

17. $9\frac{4}{5} + 5\frac{1}{4} =$

18. $3\frac{1}{5} + 4\frac{3}{7} =$

19. $2\frac{3}{4} + 6\frac{5}{6} =$

20. $6\frac{5}{8} + 1\frac{3}{10} =$

21. $2\frac{5}{7} + 5\frac{1}{4} =$

22. $1\frac{3}{4} + 2\frac{5}{9} =$

23. $7\frac{4}{7} + 2\frac{1}{2} =$

24. $6\frac{3}{8} + 2\frac{1}{3} =$

25. $2\frac{3}{4} + 4\frac{7}{10} =$

26. $3\frac{5}{7} + 8\frac{7}{10} =$

27. $5\frac{3}{4} + 4\frac{1}{3} =$

28. $4\frac{5}{6} + 7\frac{3}{10} =$

29. $4\frac{3}{5} + 2\frac{4}{9} =$

30. $2\frac{1}{5} + 6\frac{7}{12} =$

Situation Solving

Work Here

1. Tom's father owns two farms. One farm has $95\frac{1}{3}$ ha, the other $106\frac{1}{2}$ ha. How many hectares does Tom's father own?

2. John caught 4 large fish. They weighed $\frac{3}{4}$ kg, $1\frac{2}{3}$ kg, $\frac{7}{8}$ kg and 2 kg. How many kilograms of fish did he catch?

3. Betty bought 4 remnants of cloth. One contained $4\frac{1}{3}$ m, another $2\frac{3}{4}$ m, the third $5\frac{5}{8}$ m, and the fourth $5\frac{1}{2}$ m. How many metres of material did she buy?

4. Bill ate $\frac{1}{3}$ of a pie and his brother ate $\frac{1}{5}$. How much of the pie did the boys eat?

5. Mrs. Andrews used $1\frac{1}{2}$ L of sugar in a cake and $\frac{3}{4}$ L in a pie. How much sugar did she use?

6. The Jones family purchased meat from the food packers. During the past 8 months they bought $68\frac{1}{2}$ kg, $59\frac{3}{4}$ kg, $74\frac{5}{8}$ kg and $53\frac{7}{8}$ kg. How much meat did they buy?

7. In February Dave worked $170\frac{1}{4}$ h. In March he worked $163\frac{5}{8}$ h. How many hours did he work in both months?

Test Your Skill

1. Add:

(a) $\dfrac{1}{3} + \dfrac{1}{4} =$

(b) $\dfrac{1}{2} + \dfrac{1}{4} =$

(c) $\dfrac{5}{9} + \dfrac{1}{3} =$

(d) $\dfrac{2}{3} + \dfrac{1}{6} =$

(e) $2\dfrac{1}{2} + 5\dfrac{1}{4} =$

(f) $3\dfrac{1}{3} + 4\dfrac{1}{6} =$

(g) $5\dfrac{1}{4} + 7\dfrac{5}{12} =$

(h) $10\dfrac{2}{5} + 8\dfrac{1}{4} =$

(i) $4\dfrac{5}{8} + 3\dfrac{5}{6} =$

(j) $2\dfrac{4}{5} + 1\dfrac{1}{2} =$

(k) $1\dfrac{3}{4} + 1\dfrac{2}{3} =$

(l) $3\dfrac{1}{2} + 2\dfrac{2}{3} =$

(m) $\begin{array}{r} 1\dfrac{3}{4} \\ +1\dfrac{2}{5} \\ \hline \end{array}$

(n) $\begin{array}{r} 1\dfrac{2}{3} \\ +7\dfrac{3}{5} \\ \hline \end{array}$

(o) $\begin{array}{r} 2\dfrac{5}{8} \\ +3\dfrac{5}{6} \\ \hline \end{array}$

(p) $\begin{array}{r} \dfrac{5}{6} \\ +\dfrac{1}{4} \\ \hline \end{array}$

(q) $\begin{array}{r} 2\dfrac{1}{2} \\ +4\dfrac{4}{5} \\ \hline \end{array}$

(r) $\begin{array}{r} 17\dfrac{6}{7} \\ +\ 3\dfrac{1}{4} \\ \hline \end{array}$

(s) $\begin{array}{r} 8\dfrac{7}{9} \\ +\ 2\dfrac{1}{2} \\ \hline \end{array}$

(t) $\begin{array}{r} 3\dfrac{1}{4} \\ +\ 7\dfrac{2}{6} \\ \hline \end{array}$

(u) $\begin{array}{r} 6\dfrac{2}{3} \\ +\ 4\dfrac{4}{6} \\ \hline \end{array}$

(v) $\begin{array}{r} 4\dfrac{5}{6} \\ +\ 2\dfrac{3}{9} \\ \hline \end{array}$

2. What is a fraction?_____

_____

3. Write 6 mixed fractions and reduce to lowest terms.

4. Change $\frac{1}{4}$ to:

$$\overline{8} \ = \ \overline{16} \ = \ \overline{20} \ = \ \overline{12} \ = \ \overline{28} \ = \ \overline{24}$$

5. Write an improper fraction and change it to a mixed number.

Subtraction of Fractions

Betty went to the refrigerator and found $\frac{3}{4}$ of a pie. She ate $\frac{1}{4}$ of it. How much was left?

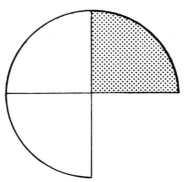

1. The entire figure above represents how much of a whole pie? _____

2. The shaded part represents the part of the pie eaten by Betty. How much did Betty eat?_____

3. The unshaded part represents the part of the pie not eaten. What fraction of the pie is not eaten?

_____or_____

$$
\begin{array}{r}
\frac{3}{4} \\
-\frac{1}{4} \\
\hline
\frac{2}{4} = \frac{1}{2}
\end{array}
\qquad \text{or} \qquad \frac{3}{4} - \frac{1}{4} = \frac{2}{4} = \frac{1}{2}
$$

Remember: A. Subtract the numerators only.

B. Reduce answers where possible to lowest terms.

Calculate the questions below:

1. $\frac{7}{8} - \frac{1}{8} =$

2. $\frac{4}{5} - \frac{1}{5} =$

3. $\frac{4}{7} - \frac{1}{7} =$

4. $\frac{9}{12} - \frac{1}{12} =$

5. $\frac{5}{8} - \frac{3}{8} =$

6. $\frac{7}{8} - \frac{3}{5} =$

7. $\frac{2}{3} - \frac{1}{3} =$

8. $\frac{9}{14} - \frac{2}{14} =$

9. $\frac{12}{21} - \frac{5}{21} =$

10. $\frac{9}{10} - \frac{4}{10} =$

11. $\frac{7}{13} - \frac{3}{13} =$

12. $\frac{4}{9} - \frac{1}{9} =$

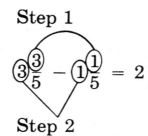

Step 1

Step 2

$$3\tfrac{3}{5} - 1\tfrac{1}{5} = 2\tfrac{2}{5}$$

Step 1: Subtract the numerators.

Step 2: Subtract the whole numbers.

Step 3: Reduce the answer (if necessary).

1. $2\tfrac{2}{3}$
    $-1\tfrac{1}{3}$

2. $6\tfrac{4}{9}$
    $-2\tfrac{2}{9}$

3. $6\tfrac{3}{5}$
    $-2\tfrac{1}{5}$

4. $3\tfrac{5}{7}$
    $-1\tfrac{4}{7}$

5. $6\tfrac{11}{15}$
    $-2\tfrac{4}{15}$

6. $3\tfrac{5}{9}$
    $-1\tfrac{1}{9}$

7. $4\tfrac{4}{7}$
    $-2\tfrac{2}{7}$

8. $3\tfrac{4}{5}$
    $-1\tfrac{2}{5}$

9. $8\tfrac{8}{15} - 5\tfrac{7}{15} =$

10. $4\tfrac{7}{9} - 1\tfrac{5}{9} =$

11. $4\tfrac{5}{11} - 1\tfrac{2}{11} =$

12. $7\tfrac{2}{5} - 2\tfrac{1}{5} =$

13. $8\tfrac{7}{9} - 5\tfrac{2}{9} =$

14. $6\tfrac{3}{7} - 2\tfrac{1}{7} =$

15. $6\tfrac{13}{15} - 2\tfrac{7}{15} =$

16. $8\tfrac{11}{15} - 4\tfrac{7}{15} =$

17. $16\tfrac{7}{18} - 2\tfrac{1}{18} =$

18. $4\tfrac{3}{5} - 1\tfrac{1}{5} =$

19. $32\tfrac{8}{28} - 3\tfrac{1}{28} =$

20. $14\tfrac{38}{50} - 1\tfrac{17}{50} =$

21. $4\tfrac{6}{9} - 2\tfrac{7}{9} =$

22. $7\tfrac{14}{16} - 2\tfrac{10}{16} =$

23. $9\tfrac{6}{40} - 2\tfrac{4}{40} =$

Finding the common denominator to subtract:

> Only fractions with like denominators can be subtracted.

Study the examples below.

$$\frac{3}{4} = \frac{9}{12}$$
$$-\frac{1}{3} = \frac{4}{12}$$
$$\frac{5}{12}$$

Step 1: Find the common denominator.
Step 2: Find the correct numerator for each fraction.
Step 3: Subtract the numerator only.
Step 4: Reduce the answer (if necessary).

and

$$\frac{5}{6} = \frac{5}{6}$$
$$-\frac{1}{2} = \frac{3}{6}$$
$$\frac{2}{6} = \frac{1}{3}$$

Calculate:

1. $\frac{1}{2}$ $-\frac{1}{8}$

2. $\frac{2}{5}$ $-\frac{1}{10}$

3. $\frac{3}{4}$ $-\frac{2}{3}$

4. $\frac{1}{4}$ $-\frac{1}{6}$

5. $\frac{1}{4}$ $-\frac{3}{16}$

6. $\frac{1}{2}$ $-\frac{1}{5}$

7. $\frac{3}{4}$ $-\frac{3}{5}$

8. $\frac{7}{10}$ $-\frac{3}{5}$

9. $\frac{1}{3}$ $-\frac{1}{4}$

10. $\frac{5}{8}$ $-\frac{1}{3}$

11. $\frac{6}{7}$ $-\frac{2}{3}$

12. $\frac{2}{3}$ $-\frac{1}{2}$

13. $\frac{5}{6}$ $-\frac{2}{3}$

14. $\frac{5}{16}$ $-\frac{1}{4}$

15. $\frac{4}{5}$ $-\frac{1}{2}$

16. $\frac{5}{6}$ $-\frac{4}{5}$

Subtracting mixed numbers:

$$5\frac{4}{5} = 5\frac{16}{20}$$
$$-3\frac{3}{4} = 3\frac{15}{20}$$
$$2\frac{1}{20}$$

Step 1: Find the common denominator.
Step 2: Find the correct numerator for each fraction.
Step 3: Subtract the numerators.
Step 4: Subtract the whole numbers.
Step 5: Reduce the answer (if necessary).

1. $\quad 4\frac{17}{20}$
   $\quad -2\frac{3}{4}$

2. $\quad 2\frac{3}{4}$
   $\quad -1\frac{1}{6}$

3. $\quad 4\frac{1}{2}$
   $\quad -2\frac{2}{5}$

4. $\quad 7\frac{7}{12}$
   $\quad -4\frac{3}{8}$

5. $\quad 6\frac{7}{8}$
   $\quad -3\frac{2}{3}$

6. $\quad 8\frac{7}{8}$
   $\quad -3\frac{5}{16}$

7. $\quad 3\frac{5}{6}$
   $\quad -1\frac{3}{4}$

8. $\quad 3\frac{3}{4}$
   $\quad -1\frac{1}{3}$

9. $\quad 5\frac{8}{9}$
   $\quad -1\frac{2}{3}$

10. $\quad 5\frac{11}{12}$
    $\quad -3\frac{2}{3}$

11. $\quad 5\frac{3}{5}$
    $\quad -3\frac{2}{15}$

12. $\quad 8\frac{7}{8}$
    $\quad -2\frac{1}{2}$

13. $\quad 8\frac{8}{9}$
    $\quad -1\frac{2}{3}$

14. $\quad 9\frac{7}{8}$
    $\quad -1\frac{1}{4}$

15. $\quad 14\frac{7}{9}$
    $\quad -\ 3\frac{1}{2}$

16. $\quad 5\frac{3}{7}$
    $\quad -1\frac{1}{4}$

17. $\quad 9\frac{6}{10}$
    $\quad -2\frac{1}{5}$

18. $\quad 8\frac{15}{16}$
    $\quad -2\frac{1}{4}$

19. $\quad 3\frac{6}{8}$
    $\quad -1\frac{1}{2}$

20. $\quad 15\frac{28}{30}$
    $\quad -2\frac{3}{5}$

Subtraction with borrowing:

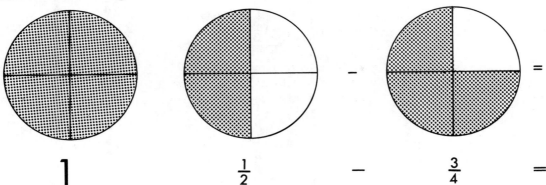

$$1 \qquad \frac{1}{2} \qquad - \qquad \frac{3}{4} \qquad =$$

1. How many quarters in 1 whole?_____

2. How many quarters in $\frac{1}{2}$?_____

3. How many quarters are there in $1\frac{1}{2}$?_____

4. How many quarters are you taking away?_____

5. How many quarters would be left?_____

$$1\frac{1}{2} = 1\frac{2}{4} = \frac{6}{4}$$
$$-\quad \frac{3}{4} = \frac{3}{4} = \frac{3}{4}$$
$$\overline{\qquad\qquad\qquad \frac{3}{4}}$$

Step 1: Find the common denominator.
Step 2: Find the correct numerator of each fraction.
Step 3: Borrow a whole number and add it to the fraction.
Step 4: Subtract the numerators.
Step 5: Reduce the answer to lowest terms (if necessary).

Study these examples:

$$5\frac{1}{3} = 5\frac{5}{15} = 4\frac{20}{15}$$
$$-1\frac{4}{5} = 1\frac{12}{15} = 1\frac{12}{15}$$
$$\overline{\qquad\qquad\qquad 3\frac{8}{15}}$$

and

$$6\frac{2}{6} = 6\frac{4}{12} = 5\frac{16}{12}$$
$$-3\frac{7}{12} = 3\frac{7}{12} = 3\frac{7}{12}$$
$$\overline{\qquad\qquad\qquad 2\frac{9}{12} = 2\frac{3}{4}}$$

Calculate the following:

1. $\quad 4\frac{1}{15}$
   $-2\frac{2}{3}$

2. $\quad 3\frac{1}{8}$
   $-1\frac{3}{5}$

3. $\quad 4\frac{1}{8}$
   $-1\frac{3}{9}$

4. $\quad 4\frac{1}{2}$
   $-1\frac{3}{4}$

5. $\quad 3\frac{2}{3}$
   $-1\frac{13}{15}$

6. $\quad 4\frac{1}{2}$
   $-1\frac{2}{3}$

7. $\quad 2\frac{1}{8}$
   $-\quad\frac{3}{4}$

8. $\quad 5\frac{1}{8}$
   $-3\frac{3}{4}$

9. $\quad 7\frac{5}{8}$
   $-5\frac{5}{6}$

10. $\quad 1\frac{1}{3}$
    $-\quad\frac{5}{6}$

73

11. $\quad 4\frac{1}{4}$
$\quad\ -2\frac{11}{16}$

12. $\quad 3\frac{3}{8}$
$\quad\ -1\frac{1}{2}$

13. $\quad 4\frac{1}{2}$
$\quad\ -1\frac{2}{3}$

14. $\quad 7\frac{1}{4}$
$\quad\ -3\frac{5}{6}$

15. $\quad 9\frac{2}{9}$
$\quad\ -4\frac{5}{6}$

16. $\quad 7\frac{2}{3}$
$\quad\ -2\frac{11}{12}$

17. $\quad 7\frac{1}{4}$
$\quad\ -2\frac{1}{2}$

18. $\quad 4\frac{1}{5}$
$\quad\ -2\frac{1}{2}$

19. $\quad 9\frac{2}{9}$
$\quad\ -3\frac{5}{6}$

20. $\quad 7\frac{5}{8}$
$\quad\ -2\frac{4}{5}$

21. $\quad 6\frac{3}{8}$
$\quad\ -2\frac{5}{6}$

22. $\quad 5\frac{1}{4}$
$\quad\ -2\frac{5}{8}$

23. $\quad 3\frac{3}{4}$
$\quad\ -1\frac{4}{5}$

24. $\quad 9\frac{5}{8}$
$\quad\ -7\frac{2}{3}$

25. $\quad 8\frac{5}{12}$
$\quad\ -4\frac{7}{8}$

26. $\quad 3\frac{1}{3}$
$\quad\ -1\frac{1}{4}$

27. $\quad 9\frac{1}{4}$
$\quad\ -3\frac{7}{12}$

28. $\quad 8\frac{2}{3}$
$\quad\ -1\frac{8}{9}$

29. $\quad 6\frac{3}{8}$
$\quad\ -4\frac{3}{5}$

30. $\quad 7\frac{2}{5}$
$\quad\ -1\frac{7}{10}$

31. $\quad 8\frac{2}{7}$
$\quad\ -4\frac{2}{3}$

32. $\quad 5\frac{1}{2}$
$\quad\ -2\frac{2}{3}$

33. $\quad 7\frac{1}{4}$
$\quad\ -3\frac{1}{2}$

34. $\quad 6\frac{1}{2}$
$\quad\ -3\frac{5}{8}$

35. $\quad 9\frac{3}{4}$
$\quad\ -2\frac{6}{7}$

36. $\quad 8\frac{1}{2}$
$\quad\ -2\frac{9}{14}$

37. $\quad 3\frac{1}{4}$
$\quad\ -1\frac{1}{3}$

38. $\quad 4\frac{7}{15}$
$\quad\ -1\frac{2}{3}$

39. $\quad 10\frac{3}{8}$
$\quad\ -3\frac{5}{6}$

40. $\quad 7\frac{3}{8}$
$\quad\ -4\frac{7}{9}$

41. $9\frac{3}{10} - 5\frac{4}{7} =$

42. $9\frac{3}{8} - 4\frac{3}{5} =$

43. $5\frac{1}{2} - 3\frac{2}{3} =$

44. $8\frac{5}{14} - 6\frac{3}{7} =$

45. $12\frac{1}{12} - 8\frac{3}{8} =$

46. $5\frac{1}{2} - 2\frac{3}{4} =$

Situation Solving

1. Catherine lives $\frac{3}{4}$ km from school. Susan lives $1\frac{1}{3}$ km from school. How much further does Susan live from the school than Catherine?

2. Bob spends $5\frac{1}{3}$ h on homework each week. Tom spends $3\frac{7}{8}$ h each week. How much more time does Bob spend on homework than Tom?

3. Howard used $20\frac{1}{8}$ L of gasoline on his trip to the country. Jim used $19\frac{2}{3}$ L of gasoline on the same trip. How much more gasoline did Howard use than Jim?

4. Lee read a book in $2\frac{3}{4}$ h. Mary read the same book in $3\frac{1}{16}$ h. How much longer did it take Mary to read the book?

5. Tony has a board $6\frac{2}{3}$ m long. If he cuts off $2\frac{3}{4}$ m, what is the length of the board that is left?

6. Walt, Tom and Ingrid have a combined weight of $107\frac{1}{3}$ kg. Tom weighs $32\frac{7}{8}$ kg and Susan weighs $31\frac{1}{8}$ kg. How much does Walt weigh?

75

Test Your Skill

	A	B	C	D
	$\frac{1}{2}$	$2\frac{3}{4}$	$\frac{7}{5}$	$\frac{2}{4}$

1. What is the denominator in fraction A?_____

2. What is the numerator in fraction B?_____

3. From the fractions above give an example of:

   (a) a fraction that can be reduced._____

   (b) a proper fraction._____

   (c) two fractions in lowest terms._____

   (d) a mixed fraction._____

   (e) an improper fraction._____

4. Subtract these questions.

(a) $\frac{4}{5}$ $-\frac{1}{5}$

(b) $\frac{7}{8}$ $-\frac{3}{8}$

(c) $\frac{9}{10}$ $-\frac{3}{10}$

(d) $\frac{8}{9}$ $-\frac{5}{9}$

(e) $2\frac{2}{3}$ $-1\frac{1}{3}$

(f) $9\frac{3}{4}$ $-1\frac{1}{4}$

(g) $8\frac{7}{8}$ $-2\frac{5}{8}$

(h) $7\frac{7}{10}$ $-1\frac{3}{10}$

(i) $\frac{1}{2}$ $-\frac{1}{8}$

(j) $\frac{3}{5}$ $-\frac{1}{3}$

(k) $\frac{5}{6}$ $-\frac{2}{3}$

(l) $\frac{7}{8}$ $-\frac{1}{3}$

(m) $6\frac{7}{8}$ $-4\frac{1}{3}$

(n) $9\frac{5}{6}$ $-3\frac{1}{4}$

(o) $8\frac{3}{4}$ $-4\frac{1}{8}$

(p) $19\frac{4}{5}$ $-13\frac{1}{4}$

(q) $5\frac{1}{2}$ $-2\frac{3}{4}$

(r) $8\frac{1}{3}$ $-4\frac{5}{6}$

(s) $9\frac{1}{8}$ $-2\frac{2}{3}$

(t) $6\frac{2}{5}$ $-1\frac{2}{3}$

Multiplication of Fractions

1. Betty's recipe for muffins called for ½ L of sugar. She wanted to increase the recipe so that it would serve 5 times as many people as the single recipe. How much sugar would she require? Betty added one-half five times to get her answer.

 $\dfrac{1}{2}$

 $\dfrac{1}{2}$

 $\dfrac{1}{2}$

 $\dfrac{1}{2}$

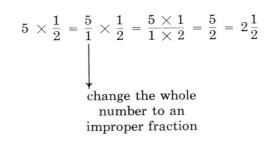

Betty's teacher showed her an easier way to get the answer.

$$5 \times \frac{1}{2} = \frac{5}{1} \times \frac{1}{2} = \frac{5 \times 1}{1 \times 2} = \frac{5}{2} = 2\frac{1}{2}$$

change the whole number to an improper fraction

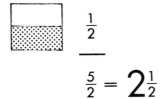 $\dfrac{1}{2}$

$$\dfrac{5}{2} = 2\tfrac{1}{2}$$

Betty needed 2½ L of sugar.

2. If Betty's recipe needed ¾ L of flour, how much flour would the increased recipe require?

$$5 \times \frac{3}{4} = \frac{5}{1} \times \frac{3}{4} = \frac{5 \times 3}{1 \times 4} = \frac{15}{4} = 3\frac{3}{4}$$

Betty needed 3¾ L of flour.

Work the examples below:

1. $\frac{1}{4} \times 3 =$ 10. $3 \times \frac{3}{8} =$

2. $\frac{3}{16} \times 5 =$ 11. $\frac{2}{5} \times 4 =$

3. $\frac{4}{5} \times 9 =$ 12. $\frac{3}{4} \times 7 =$

4. $\frac{1}{3} \times 5 =$ 13. $5 \times \frac{5}{6} =$

5. $\frac{2}{5} \times 2 =$ 14. $7 \times \frac{2}{3} =$

6. $\frac{1}{3} \times 7 =$ 15. $\frac{5}{6} \times 5 =$

7. $\frac{1}{4} \times 9 =$ 16. $9 \times \frac{3}{5} =$

8. $\frac{2}{3} \times 8 =$ 17. $\frac{2}{5} \times 6 =$

9. $\frac{3}{4} \times 5 =$ 18. $\frac{7}{8} \times 7 =$

When they started their second recipe they found an easier way to multiply fractions. One of the pupils showed the class what to do. It was called <u>cancellation</u>.

Example A: $\frac{3}{5} \times 15 = \frac{3}{\cancel{5}_1} \times \frac{\cancel{15}^3}{1} = \frac{9}{1} = 9$

Example B: $\frac{7}{8} \times 4 = \frac{7}{\cancel{8}_2} \times \frac{\cancel{4}^1}{1} = \frac{7}{2} = 3\frac{1}{2}$

Rule: When cancelling, divide the numerator and the denominator by the same number.

Use cancellation to solve the following:

1. $\frac{1}{2} \times 6 =$

2. $\frac{1}{3} \times 9 =$

3. $\frac{1}{5} \times 15 =$

4. $16 \times \frac{1}{8} =$

5. $\frac{1}{7} \times 14 =$

6. $12 \times \frac{1}{2} =$

7. $36 \times \frac{7}{9} =$

15. $27 \times \frac{2}{3} =$

17. $\frac{7}{8} \times 72 =$

8. $42 \times \frac{5}{6} =$

9. $28 \times \frac{3}{4} =$

10. $\frac{2}{3} \times 18 =$

11. $24 \times \frac{5}{6} =$

12. $160 \times \frac{3}{16} =$

13. $\frac{5}{12} \times 108 =$

14. $\frac{9}{8} \times 64 =$

16. $\frac{4}{5} \times 45 =$

18. $\frac{3}{12} \times 144 =$

Study the examples and multiply the following problems. Be sure all answers are reduced to lowest terms.

Example A: $\dfrac{1}{2} \times \dfrac{3}{4} = \dfrac{1 \times 3}{2 \times 4} = \dfrac{3}{8}$

Example B: $\dfrac{3}{5} \times \dfrac{15}{16} = \dfrac{3 \times \overset{3}{\cancel{15}}}{\underset{1}{\cancel{5}} \times 16} = \dfrac{9}{16}$

Example C: $\dfrac{3}{5} \times \dfrac{10}{24} = \dfrac{\overset{1}{\cancel{3}} \times \overset{2}{\cancel{10}}}{\underset{1}{\cancel{5}} \times \underset{8}{\cancel{24}}} = \dfrac{2}{8} = \dfrac{1}{4}$

1. $\dfrac{2}{3} \times \dfrac{1}{2} =$

2. $\dfrac{1}{6} \times \dfrac{3}{4} =$

3. $\dfrac{6}{11} \times \dfrac{2}{9} =$

4. $\dfrac{5}{15} \times \dfrac{6}{10} =$

5. $\dfrac{18}{24} \times \dfrac{11}{27} =$

6. $\dfrac{15}{16} \times \dfrac{6}{10} =$

7. $\dfrac{6}{8} \times \dfrac{7}{9} =$

8. $\dfrac{9}{15} \times \dfrac{10}{12} =$

9. $\dfrac{3}{8} \times \dfrac{12}{15} =$

10. $\dfrac{4}{7} \times \dfrac{14}{20} =$

11. $\dfrac{3}{5} \times \dfrac{5}{9} =$

12. $\dfrac{4}{5} \times \dfrac{20}{32} =$

13. $\dfrac{9}{15} \times \dfrac{5}{6} =$

14. $\dfrac{6}{12} \times \dfrac{3}{9} =$

15. $\dfrac{7}{14} \times \dfrac{28}{21} =$

16. $\dfrac{4}{9} \times \dfrac{36}{40} =$

17. $\dfrac{3}{16} \times \dfrac{6}{21} =$

18. $\dfrac{9}{12} \times \dfrac{3}{18} =$

19. $\dfrac{6}{7} \times \dfrac{21}{80} =$

20. $\dfrac{14}{15} \times \dfrac{15}{41} =$

21. $\dfrac{5}{12} \times \dfrac{6}{10} =$

22. $\dfrac{30}{60} \times \dfrac{30}{60} =$

23. $\dfrac{14}{32} \times \dfrac{16}{42} =$

24. $\dfrac{20}{14} \times \dfrac{30}{90} =$

Remember: 1. Cancellation is a short cut.

2. In cancellation a numerator and a denominator are divided by the same number.

3. Cancellation is really reducing the product to lowest terms *before* multiplying rather than *after*.

Example A: $\dfrac{3}{4} \times \dfrac{8}{9} = \dfrac{3 \times 8}{4 \times 9} = \dfrac{24}{36} = \dfrac{24 \div 12}{36 \div 12} = \dfrac{2}{3}$ → Cancellation *after* multiplication

Example B: $\dfrac{3}{4} \times \dfrac{8}{9} = \dfrac{\overset{1}{\cancel{3}} \times \overset{2}{\cancel{8}}}{\underset{1}{\cancel{4}} \times \underset{3}{\cancel{9}}} = \dfrac{1 \times 2}{1 \times 3} = \dfrac{2}{3}$ → Cancellation *before* multiplication

Use cancellation to multiply the following:

1. (a) $\dfrac{2}{3} \times \dfrac{3}{4} =$ (b) $\dfrac{7}{9} \times \dfrac{3}{14} =$ (c) $\dfrac{8}{10} \times \dfrac{5}{16} =$

Cancellation can also be used when multiplying more than two fractions.

2. (a) $\dfrac{2}{9} \times \dfrac{6}{4} \times \dfrac{2}{3} =$ (b) $\dfrac{6}{18} \times \dfrac{24}{30} \times \dfrac{5}{12} =$

(c) $\dfrac{7}{14} \times \dfrac{21}{28} \times \dfrac{7}{14} =$ (d) $\dfrac{3}{2} \times \dfrac{4}{9} \times \dfrac{9}{6} =$

3. (a) $\dfrac{4}{20} \times \dfrac{10}{16} \times \dfrac{4}{10} =$ (b) $\dfrac{5}{12} \times \dfrac{3}{4} \times \dfrac{16}{20} =$

(c) $\dfrac{2}{4} \times \dfrac{6}{8} \times \dfrac{2}{10} =$ (d) $\dfrac{6}{7} \times \dfrac{14}{20} \times \dfrac{21}{18} =$

4. (a) $\dfrac{2}{8} \times \dfrac{6}{9} \times \dfrac{3}{4} \times \dfrac{2}{6} =$ (b) $\dfrac{7}{8} \times \dfrac{2}{3} \times \dfrac{3}{4} \times \dfrac{16}{14} =$

(c) $\dfrac{9}{4} \times \dfrac{8}{27} \times \dfrac{3}{5} \times \dfrac{15}{18} =$ (d) $\dfrac{4}{6} \times \dfrac{3}{3} \times \dfrac{12}{9} \times \dfrac{6}{8} =$

5. (a) $\dfrac{6}{7} \times \dfrac{14}{12} \times \dfrac{3}{15} \times \dfrac{6}{9} =$ (b) $\dfrac{2}{3} \times \dfrac{3}{4} \times \dfrac{5}{6} \times \dfrac{12}{20} =$

(c) $\dfrac{6}{14} \times \dfrac{7}{8} \times \dfrac{16}{20} \times \dfrac{10}{12} =$ (d) $\dfrac{8}{10} \times \dfrac{6}{8} \times \dfrac{40}{8} \times \dfrac{4}{16} =$

6. (a) $\dfrac{6}{8} \times \dfrac{4}{5} \times \dfrac{15}{24} \times \dfrac{16}{15} =$ (b) $\dfrac{6}{7} \times \dfrac{9}{8} \times \dfrac{28}{30} \times \dfrac{12}{18} =$

(c) $\dfrac{4}{14} \times \dfrac{7}{9} \times \dfrac{3}{10} \times \dfrac{5}{8} =$ (d) $\dfrac{5}{18} \times \dfrac{7}{12} \times \dfrac{6}{7} \times \dfrac{9}{10} =$

The pupils in the cooking class found that they could not multiply a mixed number by a fraction. After experimenting they found that they could change the mixed number to an improper fraction and then multiply.

Example A:

$$4\frac{1}{2} = \frac{9}{2}$$

1 whole $= \frac{2}{2}$

4 wholes $= \frac{8}{2}$ $\quad = \frac{8}{2} + \frac{1}{2} = \frac{9}{2}$

Example B: $2\frac{5}{6} = \frac{17}{6}$

Example C: $4\frac{7}{8} = \frac{39}{8}$

Practise changing the mixed numbers to improper fractions:

1. $3\frac{1}{4} =$

2. $6\frac{1}{2} =$

3. $9\frac{2}{3} =$

4. $7\frac{1}{4} =$

5. $2\frac{3}{4} =$

6. $4\frac{1}{5} =$

7. $9\frac{2}{7} =$

8. $8\frac{4}{5} =$

9. $5\frac{3}{8} =$

10. $3\frac{6}{7} =$

11. $4\frac{7}{9} =$

12. $3\frac{6}{8} =$

13. $10\frac{1}{4} =$

14. $5\frac{3}{4} =$

15. $12\frac{1}{5} =$

16. $14\frac{2}{3} =$

17. $15\frac{1}{3} =$

18. $23\frac{3}{5} =$

Here is an easier way.

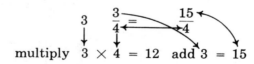

multiply $3 \times 4 = 12$ add 3 $= 15$

Use the easy method to change the mixed numbers to improper fractions:

1. $9\frac{1}{4} =$

2. $6\frac{2}{3} =$

3. $3\frac{2}{5} =$

4. $4\frac{4}{7} =$

5. $5\frac{7}{8} =$

6. $2\frac{9}{10} =$

7. $3\frac{3}{7} =$

8. $6\frac{4}{5} =$

9. $12\frac{1}{3} =$

10. $16\frac{1}{2} =$

11. $4\frac{10}{11} =$

12. $6\frac{4}{9} =$

Using what you have learned about changing mixed numbers to improper fractions, study the examples below.

Example A: $\left(3\frac{1}{2}\right) \times \left(3\right) = \frac{7}{2} \times \frac{3}{1} = \frac{21}{2} = 10\frac{1}{2}$

Step 1: Change the multiplicand to an improper fraction.

Example B: $2\frac{5}{8} \times \frac{2}{7} = \frac{21}{8} \times \frac{2}{7} =$

Step 2: Change the multiplier to an improper fraction.

Example C: $2\frac{1}{3} \times 1\frac{1}{2} = \frac{}{3} \times \frac{}{2} =$

Step 3: Multiply.

Multiply the following fractions.

> Remember: OF means the same as multiply.

1. $1\frac{3}{4}$ of 8 =

2. $10 \times 4\frac{1}{2} =$

3. $3\frac{2}{3}$ of 18 =

4. $12 \times 2\frac{3}{4} =$

5. $4\frac{1}{2} \times \frac{2}{3} =$

6. $\frac{3}{8} \times 2\frac{6}{9} =$

7. $6\frac{2}{3} \times \frac{6}{10} =$

8. $\frac{7}{8} \times 3\frac{1}{5} =$

9. $3\frac{3}{4} \times 2\frac{2}{3} =$

10. $1\frac{1}{4} \times 2\frac{2}{5} =$

11. $2\frac{1}{3} \times 2\frac{1}{2} =$

12. $2\frac{4}{7} \times 8\frac{3}{4} =$

13. $1\frac{1}{5} \times \frac{1}{6} =$

14. $16 \times 2\frac{1}{4} =$

15. $3\frac{1}{3} \times 2\frac{1}{4} =$

16. $3\frac{3}{5}$ of 15 =

17. $\frac{16}{27} \times 2\frac{5}{32} =$

18. $7\frac{2}{3}$ of 9 =

19. $5\frac{1}{2} \times 3\frac{3}{11} =$

20. $3\frac{1}{4} \times \frac{8}{39} =$

21. $12 \times 8\frac{3}{4} =$

22. $5\frac{2}{5} \times 4\frac{1}{6} =$

23. $6\frac{4}{5} \times \frac{10}{17} =$

24. $4\frac{1}{12} \times 3\frac{3}{7} =$

Test Your Skill

1. Cancel:

   (a) $\dfrac{7 \times 3 \times 16 \times 45}{9 \times 4 \times 35 \times 39} =$ (b) $\dfrac{8}{9} \times \dfrac{4}{7} \times \dfrac{28}{40} \times \dfrac{27}{32} =$

2. Change from improper fractions to mixed numbers:

   (a) $\dfrac{7}{2} =$ (d) $\dfrac{6}{2} =$ (g) $\dfrac{14}{6} =$

   (b) $\dfrac{9}{4} =$ (e) $\dfrac{7}{2} =$ (h) $\dfrac{6}{4} =$

   (c) $\dfrac{3}{2} =$ (f) $\dfrac{12}{5} =$ (i) $\dfrac{28}{4} =$

3. Change from mixed numbers to improper fractions:

   (a) $2\dfrac{1}{2} =$ (d) $14\dfrac{2}{3} =$ (g) $15\dfrac{3}{10} =$

   (b) $6\dfrac{3}{4} =$ (e) $7\dfrac{7}{9} =$ (h) $23\dfrac{1}{2} =$

   (c) $9\dfrac{1}{3} =$ (f) $4\dfrac{5}{8} =$ (i) $30\dfrac{1}{3} =$

4. Multiply the following.

   (a) $\dfrac{3}{4} \times 2\dfrac{2}{3} =$ (l) $4\dfrac{1}{4} \times \dfrac{8}{39} =$

   (b) $2\dfrac{1}{3} \times 3\dfrac{1}{5} =$ (m) $\dfrac{6}{25} \times 2\dfrac{1}{12} =$

   (c) $2\dfrac{2}{3} \times 1\dfrac{4}{5} =$ (n) $1\dfrac{7}{8} \times 3\dfrac{1}{5} =$

   (d) $1\dfrac{2}{3} \times 1\dfrac{1}{5} =$ (o) $1\dfrac{1}{4} \times 2\dfrac{2}{5} =$

   (e) $3\dfrac{1}{3} \times 2\dfrac{1}{4} =$ (p) $3\dfrac{1}{8} \times 6\dfrac{2}{3} =$

   (f) $2\dfrac{2}{5} \times 42\dfrac{1}{2} =$ (q) $4\dfrac{1}{3} \times 5\dfrac{2}{9} =$

   (g) $1\dfrac{4}{7} \times 2\dfrac{1}{3} =$ (r) $8\dfrac{3}{7} \times 1\dfrac{1}{5} =$

   (h) $5\dfrac{1}{2} \times 5\dfrac{1}{2} =$ (s) $3\dfrac{1}{6} \times 5 =$

   (i) $2\dfrac{4}{7} \times 8\dfrac{3}{4} =$ (t) $6\dfrac{1}{4} \times \dfrac{4}{25} =$

   (j) $2\dfrac{1}{3} \times 2\dfrac{1}{2} =$ (u) $\dfrac{3}{9} \times \dfrac{12}{15} =$

   (k) $3\dfrac{3}{4} \times \dfrac{15}{16} =$ (v) $6\dfrac{2}{3} \times 10 =$

Division of Fractions

The Sewing Class had $6\frac{1}{4}$ m of cotton. They wanted to make 5 aprons. The teacher showed the class how to find the number of metres to be used for each apron. This is what she put on the board.

$$6\frac{1}{4} \div 5$$

change to an improper fraction $\left(\right)$ change to a fraction

$$\frac{25}{4} \div \frac{5}{1}$$

multiply $\Big)$ invert the divisor   (*invert* means *turn upside down*)

$$\frac{\overset{5}{\cancel{25}}}{4} \times \frac{1}{\cancel{5}} = \frac{5}{4} = 1\frac{1}{4}$$ m of material could be used for each apron.

1. Fill in the chart.

Question		Fractional Form		Invert-Multiply		Answer
$3\frac{1}{3} \div 2$	$=$	$\frac{10}{3} \div \frac{2}{1}$	$=$	$\frac{10}{3} \times \frac{1}{2} = \frac{5}{3}$	$=$	$1\frac{2}{3}$
$6\frac{3}{5} \div 3$	$=$	$\frac{33}{5} \div \frac{3}{1}$	$=$	$\frac{33}{5} \times \frac{1}{3}$		
$8\frac{2}{6} \div 10$	$=$	$\frac{50}{6} \div \frac{10}{1}$				
$7\frac{1}{2} \div 5$						
$9\frac{1}{3} \div 7$						

2. Divide. Cancel when possible:

(a) $3\frac{1}{4} \div 2 =$

(b) $4\frac{1}{2} \div 3 =$

(c) $1\frac{2}{3} \div 2 =$

(d) $1\frac{1}{5} \div 4 =$

(h) $8\frac{3}{4} \div 7 =$

(i) $4\frac{1}{2} \div 5 =$

(j) $4\frac{9}{10} \div 7 =$

(k) $8\frac{4}{5} \div 16 =$

(e) $11\frac{1}{2} \div 6 =$

(l) $8\frac{3}{8} \div 5 =$

(f) $5\frac{3}{7} \div 5 =$

(m) $13\frac{3}{5} \div 6 =$

(g) $9\frac{1}{2} \div 4 =$

(n) $16\frac{4}{9} \div 12 =$

3. Mary bought $2\frac{1}{4}$ kg of candy for a party. If 15 girls attended the party, how much candy did each girl get?	
4. On a hunting trip Jack walked $12\frac{1}{2}$ km in 5 h. How many kilometres an hour did he average?	
5. Bill's motorcycle held $12\frac{1}{2}$ L of gasoline. If he used an average of 4 L a week, how long would it be until he had to purchase gas?	
6. The girls in the Sewing Class have $7\frac{1}{2}$ m of cotton to make 3 skirts. How much material can they use for each skirt?	

The method of inverting the divisor and multiplying is also used when the divisor is a mixed number or a fraction. Study the examples below.

Example A:

$$2\frac{2}{5} \div 1\frac{4}{5}$$

change to an improper fraction

$$\frac{12}{5} \div \frac{9}{5}$$

change to an improper fraction

multiply invert

$$\frac{\overset{4}{\cancel{12}}}{\cancel{5}} \times \frac{\cancel{5}}{\cancel{9}} = \frac{4}{3} = 1\frac{1}{3}$$

Example B:

$$3\frac{1}{3} \div \frac{2}{3} = \frac{10}{3} \div \frac{2}{3} = \frac{\overset{5}{\cancel{10}}}{\cancel{3}} \times \frac{\cancel{3}}{\cancel{2}} = 5$$

Divide. Be sure to cancel if possible:

1. $2\frac{1}{3} \div \frac{4}{5} =$

2. $4\frac{1}{5} \div 1\frac{1}{3} =$

3. $1\frac{2}{7} \div \frac{4}{15} =$

4. $7\frac{3}{5} \div 10\frac{6}{7} =$

5. $9\frac{3}{5} \div \frac{8}{15} =$

6. $5\frac{1}{4} \div \frac{7}{10} =$

7. $2\frac{7}{8} \div 1\frac{1}{7} =$

8. $4\frac{1}{2} \div \frac{1}{5} =$

9. $4\frac{3}{4} \div 7\frac{1}{8} =$

10. $2\frac{3}{4} \div \frac{1}{8} =$

11. $2\frac{1}{5} \div 7\frac{7}{10} =$

12. $4\frac{1}{5} \div \frac{7}{10} =$

13. $1\frac{3}{7} \div 3\frac{4}{7} =$

14. $2\frac{1}{16} \div 4\frac{5}{9} =$

15. $4\frac{1}{6} \div \frac{5}{8} =$

16. $9\frac{3}{4} \div 2\frac{1}{6} =$

17. $8\frac{1}{6} \div \frac{7}{16} =$

18. $8\frac{1}{2} \div 1\frac{1}{3} =$

1. Divide:

(a) $8 \div \frac{1}{3} =$

(b) $\frac{5}{6} \div 4 =$

(c) $\frac{3}{4} \div \frac{1}{8} =$

(d) $\frac{9}{20} \div 4\frac{1}{2} =$

(e) $7\frac{1}{4} \div 2\frac{5}{12} =$

(f) $10 \div \frac{5}{10} =$

(g) $5\frac{1}{2} \div \frac{1}{3} =$

(h) $\frac{7}{16} \div 7 =$

(i) $\frac{1}{4} \div 1\frac{1}{2} =$

(j) $3\frac{1}{2} \div 5\frac{5}{6} =$

(k) $1\frac{1}{3} \div 2\frac{1}{2} =$

(l) $\frac{7}{9} \div 2\frac{1}{3} =$

(m) $\frac{3}{10} \div 2\frac{1}{2} =$

(n) $4\frac{1}{5} \div \frac{7}{8} =$

(o) $2\frac{2}{3} \div 4 =$

(p) $4\frac{3}{8} \div 2\frac{1}{12} =$

(q) $4\frac{7}{8} \div 2\frac{1}{6} =$

(r) $8\frac{1}{4} \div 1\frac{5}{6} =$

Work Here

2. Kenneth used 26 L of gasoline on his trip. This was $\frac{3}{4}$ of a tankful. How many litres of gasoline does the tank hold?	
3. The food service made $4\frac{1}{4}$ kg of cake to be served to 30 people. How large was each serving?	
4. The Sewing Class made school ribbons. Each was $\frac{2}{3}$ m long. How many ribbons could be cut from a piece of ribbon $36\frac{2}{3}$ m long?	

Test Your Skill

1. Change 5 to an improper fraction. _____

2. Change $6\frac{2}{3}$ to an improper fraction. _____

3. What is the meaning of the word *invert*? _____

   _____

4. Invert the following fractions:

   $\frac{2}{3}$ to_____, $\frac{3}{4}$ to_____, $\frac{7}{8}$ to_____, $\frac{9}{10}$ to_____.

5. Change the following mixed fractions to improper fractions and invert.

   Example: $2\frac{1}{2} = \frac{5}{2}$ to $\frac{2}{5}$

   $2\frac{1}{4} =$ _____ to _____ $5\frac{2}{5} =$ _____ to _____

   $4\frac{1}{3} =$ _____ to _____ $4\frac{5}{6} =$ _____ to _____

   $3\frac{7}{10} =$ _____ to _____ $6\frac{7}{8} =$ _____ to _____

6. (a) $8\frac{2}{5} \div 3 =$ (h) $8\frac{2}{3} \div 5 =$

   (b) $9\frac{3}{4} \div 3 =$ (i) $8 \div \frac{1}{2} =$

   (c) $10 \div \frac{2}{5} =$ (j) $\frac{3}{4} \div \frac{3}{5} =$

   (d) $\frac{5}{8} \div \frac{3}{4} =$ (k) $8\frac{1}{4} \div 2\frac{3}{4} =$

   (e) $6\frac{1}{6} \div 12\frac{1}{3} =$ (l) $2\frac{4}{5} \div 5\frac{1}{4} =$

   (f) $4\frac{3}{8} \div 1\frac{1}{8} =$ (m) $5\frac{1}{3} \div 2\frac{3}{3} =$

   (g) $\frac{1}{2} \div \frac{1}{8} =$ (n) $1\frac{7}{8} \div 11\frac{1}{4} =$

CHAPTER THREE
DECIMAL FRACTIONS

The Meaning of Decimal Fractions

A part of a whole may be expressed as a common fraction or as a decimal fraction. A decimal fraction is a part of a whole in which the denominator is not stated but understood by place value.

$$\$\frac{1}{2} \text{ may be stated as } \$ \ .50$$

$$\$\frac{1}{4} \text{ may be stated as } \$ \ .25$$

$$\$\frac{3}{4} \text{ may be stated as } \$ \ .75$$

$$\text{Therefore } \frac{1}{2} = .50 \text{ or } \frac{50}{100}$$

$$\frac{1}{4} = .25 \text{ or } \frac{25}{100}$$

$$\frac{3}{4} = .75 \text{ or } \frac{75}{100}$$

Remember: All numbers to the left of the decimal point represent whole numbers. All numbers to the right of the decimal represent fractions (part of a whole number).

whole number . part of a whole number

Study the examples below. Discuss with your teacher which digits represent whole numbers and which digits represent part (a fraction) of a whole number.

1.66	3.21	4.67
3.67	30.05	181.634
12.06	2.005	80.009
9.25	9.2	4.0
8.675	18.54	3.5
125.6	168.325	2.75

Place Value

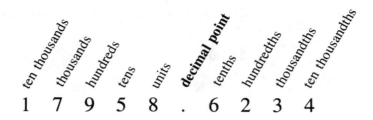

$$\begin{array}{ccccc|cccc}
\text{ten thousands} & \text{thousands} & \text{hundreds} & \text{tens} & \text{units} & \text{decimal point} & \text{tenths} & \text{hundredths} & \text{thousandths} & \text{ten thousandths} \\
1 & 7 & 9 & 5 & 8 & . & 6 & 2 & 3 & 4
\end{array}$$

Study these examples and verbally tell what each means:

Example A: 8.6 means 8 whole numbers and 6 tenths of another number or $8\frac{6}{10}$.

Example B: 58.62 means 58 whole numbers and 62 hundredths of another number or $58\frac{62}{100}$.

Discuss these as to place value:

958.6	0.623 4
8.62	8.623
958.62	17 958.6
0.623	7 958.62
7 958.623	58.623 4

> Note: When there is no digit to the left of the decimal point, a zero should be placed there to avoid error. However, in teaching decimals, the zero will not always be used in this book.

Express the following decimals as fractions:

0.5 =	2.5 =	0.8 =	2.62 =
0.6 =	2.75 =	0.9 =	3.675 =
0.75 =	3.50 =	0.92 =	3.690 =
0.8 =	15.625 =	0.82 =	14.213 =
0.36 =	9.2 =	0.73 =	15.703 =
4.69 =	5.8 =	0.62 =	118.905 =

Memorize:

$\frac{1}{2}$ = .5	$\frac{1}{5}$ = .2	$\frac{3}{8}$ = .375
$\frac{1}{4}$ = .25	$\frac{2}{5}$ = .4	$\frac{5}{8}$ = .625
$\frac{3}{4}$ = .75	$\frac{3}{5}$ = .6	$\frac{7}{8}$ = .875
$\frac{1}{3}$ = .333	$\frac{4}{5}$ = .8	
$\frac{2}{3}$ = .667	$\frac{1}{8}$ = .125	

Changing Common Fractions to Decimal Fractions

To change a common fraction to a decimal fraction, divide the numerator by the denominator.

Examples:

$$\frac{1}{2} = 2\overline{)1.0} \quad .5$$
$$\underline{1\ 0}$$
$$0\ R$$

$$\frac{1}{4} = 4\overline{)1.00} \quad .25$$
$$\underline{8}$$
$$20$$
$$\underline{20}$$
$$0\ R$$

Change the fractions to decimals (show all work):

$\frac{3}{4} =$ $\frac{7}{8} =$

$\frac{3}{5} =$ $\frac{4}{10} =$

$\frac{1}{8} =$ $\frac{6}{8} =$

Discuss: Why do the fractions $\frac{3}{4}$ and $\frac{6}{8}$ have the same decimal equivalent?

Change the common fractions or mixed fractions to decimal fractions. (Work to 3 decimal places if necessary.)

1. $\frac{1}{10} =$ $\frac{3}{10} =$ $\frac{6}{10} =$ $\frac{4}{10} =$ $\frac{5}{10} =$

2. $\frac{1}{2} =$ $\frac{3}{6} =$ $\frac{4}{8} =$ $\frac{5}{10} =$ $\frac{6}{12} =$

3. $\frac{38}{100} =$ $\frac{54}{100} =$ $\frac{87}{100} =$ $\frac{99}{100} =$ $\frac{83}{100} =$

4. $\dfrac{4}{100} =$ $\dfrac{7}{100} =$ $\dfrac{9}{100} =$ $\dfrac{5}{100} =$ $\dfrac{1}{100} =$

5. $1\dfrac{1}{2} =$ $6\dfrac{3}{4} =$ $4\dfrac{7}{8} =$ $3\dfrac{9}{10} =$ $5\dfrac{4}{5} =$

6. $3\dfrac{3}{10} =$ $9\dfrac{4}{100} =$ $6\dfrac{7}{1000} =$ $8\dfrac{37}{1000} =$ $4\dfrac{1}{4} =$

7. $\dfrac{17}{25} =$ $\dfrac{34}{50} =$ $\dfrac{75}{100} =$ $\dfrac{21}{25} =$ $18\dfrac{7}{25} =$

Now try these for extra practice.

8. $\dfrac{4}{3} =$ $\dfrac{6}{5} =$ $\dfrac{9}{4} =$ $\dfrac{5}{3} =$ $\dfrac{7}{4} =$

9. $\dfrac{6}{3} =$ $\dfrac{9}{5} =$ $\dfrac{12}{8} =$ $\dfrac{7}{3} =$ $\dfrac{8}{5} =$

10. $\dfrac{8}{3} =$ $\dfrac{5}{4} =$ $\dfrac{15}{6} =$ $\dfrac{13}{7} =$ $\dfrac{17}{2} =$

Rounding Off Decimals

To round off a decimal fraction, write it down omitting the numbers in the unwanted decimal places on the far right of the fraction. If the omitted number closest to the remaining part of the fraction was 5 or more, increase the number to its left by one. If the omitted number was less than 5, leave the number to its left as it is.

Example: .5473 rounded off to the nearest tenth is   .5
              rounded off to the nearest hundredth is   .55
              rounded off to the nearest thousandth is   .547

1. Round off the following decimals to the nearest tenth.

(a) .59 =   (f) .493 =   (k) 4.63 =   (p) 6.09 =

(b) .46 =   (g) .823 =   (l) 2.875 =   (q) 5.24 =

(c) .32 =   (h) .374 =   (m) 9.42 =   (r) 8.88 =

(d) .57 =   (i) .613 =   (n) 8.337 =   (s) 15.674 =

(e) .33 =   (j) .384 =   (o) 5.43 =   (t) 9.428 =

2. Round off the following decimals to the nearest hundredth.

(a) .049 =   (f) .095 =   (k) 3.659 =   (p) 6.309 =

(b) .563 =   (g) .448 =   (l) 8.426 =   (q) 5.272 =

(c) .327 =   (h) .932 =   (m) 9.223 =   (r) 8.628 =

(d) .446 =   (i) .657 =   (n) 4.321 =   (s) 19.678 =

(e) .325 =   (j) .367 =   (o) 8.569 =   (t) 4.005 =

3. Round off the following decimals to the nearest thousandth.

(a) .0675 =

(b) .3251 =

(c) .4529 =

(d) .5268 =

(e) .9362 =

(f) .3509 =

(g) .4262 =

(h) .5836 =

(i) .9275 =

(j) .8651 =

(k) 6.4265 =

(l) 3.6222 =

(m) 5.8729 =

(n) 3.6251 =

(o) 8.6525 =

(p) 16.2513 =

(q) 8.0094 =

(r) 3.0506 =

(s) 18.6213 =

(t) 14.5261 =

4. Round off to the nearest cent.

(a) $0.293

(b) $0.837

(c) $0.8127

(d) $0.473

(e) $0.8943

(f) $2.659

(g) $3.543

(h) $5.697

(i) $6.327

(j) $5.421

(k) $5.039

(l) $6.008

(m) $8.099

(n) $6.573

(o) $9.487

(p) $8.045

(q) $6.529

(r) $9.867

(s) $3.320

(t) $15.510

Change the following fractions to decimal fractions and round off to the nearest thousandth.

(a) $\frac{1}{3}$ =

(b) $\frac{2}{3}$ =

(c) $\frac{1}{6}$ =

(d) $\frac{5}{6}$ =

(e) $\frac{1}{7}$ =

(f) $\frac{3}{7}$ =

(g) $\frac{5}{7}$ =

(h) $\frac{4}{7}$ =

(i) $\frac{1}{9}$ =

(j) $\frac{4}{9}$ =

(k) $\frac{5}{9}$ =

(l) $\frac{7}{9}$ =

Changing Decimal Fractions to Common Fractions

To change a decimal fraction to a common fraction, write down the fraction without a decimal point to make the numerator, and put a "1" for the decimal and "0"s for each decimal place to make the denominator.

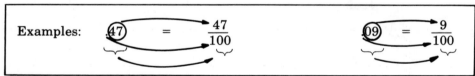

Examples: $.47 = \dfrac{47}{100}$ $.09 = \dfrac{9}{100}$

Change the following decimal fractions to common fractions and reduce to lowest terms. (Disregard the initial zeros. See note under "Place Value.")

(a) 0.5

(b) 0.75

(c) 0.25

(d) 0.50

(e) 0.8

(f) 0.95

(g) 0.85

(h) 0.825

(i) 0.875

(j) 0.625

(k) 0.125

(l) 0.2

(m) 0.4

(n) 0.6

(o) 0.20

(p) 0.65

(q) 0.9

(r) 0.715

(s) 0.036

(t) 0.009

If the decimal fraction is made up of a whole number and a decimal, follow the example below.

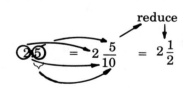

$$2.5 = 2\dfrac{5}{10} \xrightarrow{\text{reduce}} = 2\dfrac{1}{2}$$

Change the following decimal fractions to mixed fractions.

(a) 2.5

(b) 3.8

(c) 7.06

(d) 9.75

(e) 8.25

(f) 17.95

(g) 4.08

(h) 3.625

(i) 9.875

(j) 6.20

(k) 5.006

(l) 30.09

(m) 5.45

(n) 18.663

(o) 4.4

(p) 9.2

(q) 17.6

(r) 3.125

(s) 14.7

(t) 9.006

Fill in the blanks:

Decimal	Fraction
0.5	
	$\frac{1}{4}$
0.75	
0.333	
	$\frac{2}{3}$
0.2	
	$\frac{2}{5}$
	$\frac{4}{5}$
0.6	
0.125	
	$\frac{3}{8}$
	$\frac{7}{8}$
0.625	
	$\frac{1}{6}$
0.55	
0.06	
	$\frac{6}{9}$
0.66	
	$\frac{90}{100}$
	$\frac{9}{10}$
0.8	

Decimal	Fraction
0.65	
	$8\frac{1}{5}$
0.05	
	$19\frac{1}{3}$
	$6\frac{3}{5}$
2.5	
	$2\frac{1}{4}$
9.6	
	$3\frac{1}{5}$
3.06	
4.58	
1.25	
	$7\frac{1}{5}$
0.45	
3.375	
	$3\frac{4}{10}$
	$15\frac{4}{5}$
6.20	
	$9\frac{3}{5}$
0.006	
	$\frac{70}{1000}$

Match the decimal fraction with the common fraction with arrows as shown.

1.		2.		3.			4.		
$\frac{1}{2}$	0.667	0.05		$\frac{1}{5}$	$2\frac{1}{2}$	0.25	0.8		0.37
$\frac{1}{3}$	0.4	0.167		$\frac{2}{3}$	0.3	0.16	2.9		$\frac{3}{5}$
$\frac{2}{3}$	0.625	0.2		$\frac{9}{10}$	0.05	$6\frac{1}{2}$	0.01		0.1
$\frac{1}{5}$	0.125	0.3		$\frac{1}{20}$	0.04	$\frac{1}{25}$	0.035		0.003
$\frac{2}{5}$	0.5	0.4		1	4.09	$\frac{3}{10}$	0.875		$\frac{7}{8}$
$\frac{4}{5}$	0.6	0.5		$\frac{1}{6}$	$\frac{1}{4}$	6.55	$\frac{37}{100}$		$\frac{4}{5}$
$\frac{3}{5}$	0.375	0.667		$\frac{1}{2}$	2.25	2.5	$\frac{1}{3}$		$2\frac{9}{10}$
$\frac{1}{8}$	0.333	0.8		$\frac{3}{10}$	6.5	$4\frac{9}{100}$	$\frac{1}{10}$		$\frac{1}{100}$
$\frac{3}{8}$	0.8	0.9		$\frac{4}{5}$	$\frac{4}{25}$	$2\frac{1}{4}$	$\frac{3}{100}$		0.333
$\frac{5}{8}$	0.2	1.00		$\frac{2}{5}$	$6\frac{55}{100}$	$\frac{1}{20}$	0.60		$\frac{35}{1000}$

100

Comparing Decimal Fractions and Common Fractions

Circle the larger of the two.

1. 0.6 or 0.69

2. 0.06 or 0.6

3. 3.5 or 0.35

4. 6.02 or 6.2

5. 0.25 or 0.3

6. 0.66 or 0.60

7. 0.01 or 0.001

8. 4.23 or 3.24

9. 0.75 or 7.5

10. 3.2 or 0.032

11. 0.54 or 0.53

12. 2.5 or 20.25

13. 0.6 or 0.7

14. 0.93 or 0.39

15. 0.2 or 0.23

16. 3.25 or 0.22

17. 0.6 or 0.605

18. 3.2 or 2.22

19. 0.99 or 1

20. 1.02 or 0.897

Circle the smaller of the two.

1. $\frac{1}{4}$ or 0.333

2. 0.6 or $\frac{1}{3}$

3. 4.2 or $4\frac{1}{5}$

4. 2.6 or $2\frac{7}{8}$

5. 3.5 or $3\frac{50}{1000}$

6. $\frac{7}{8}$ or 0.615

7. 4.55 or $4\frac{1}{2}$

8. 9.2 or 2.9

9. $\frac{1}{5}$ or 0.15

10. $\frac{6}{8}$ or 0.73

11. $4\frac{1}{3}$ or 4.3339

12. $9\frac{1}{4}$ or 25.9

13. 5.6 or 5.06

14. 22.5 or $22\frac{1}{3}$

15. $3\frac{1}{5}$ or 3.5

16. 0.96 or $9\frac{6}{10}$

17. $8\frac{1}{4}$ or 8.333

18. $6\frac{1}{5}$ or 6.4

19. 0.006 or $\frac{6}{10}$

20. 0.05 or $\frac{5}{10}$

Addition of Decimals

When adding decimal fractions put the decimal points directly under each other.

Example: 2.45 + 0.03 + 4.05 = 6.53

$$\begin{array}{r} 2.45 \\ 0.03 \\ \underline{4.05} \\ 6.53 \end{array}$$

When a decimal answer ends in one or more zeros, you may drop them.

Examples: 2.63 + 3.17 = 5.80 or 5.8

$$\begin{array}{r} 2.63 \\ + 3.17 \\ \hline 5.80 \text{ or } 5.8 \end{array}$$

0.03 + 3.45 + 2.52 = 6.00 or 6

$$\begin{array}{r} 0.03 \\ 3.45 \\ \underline{2.52} \\ 6.00 \text{ or } 6 \end{array}$$

Add:

1.
$$\begin{array}{r} 0.4 \\ + 0.6 \end{array}$$
$$\begin{array}{r} 0.06 \\ + 0.02 \end{array}$$
$$\begin{array}{r} 4.9 \\ + 2.0 \end{array}$$
$$\begin{array}{r} 0.3 \\ + 0.6 \end{array}$$
$$\begin{array}{r} 0.36 \\ + 0.24 \end{array}$$

2.
$$\begin{array}{r} 0.09 \\ + 0.05 \end{array}$$
$$\begin{array}{r} 0.63 \\ + 0.46 \end{array}$$
$$\begin{array}{r} 0.93 \\ + 0.47 \end{array}$$
$$\begin{array}{r} 0.93 \\ + 0.87 \end{array}$$
$$\begin{array}{r} 0.45 \\ + 0.65 \end{array}$$

3.
$$\begin{array}{r} 0.53 \\ 0.47 \\ + 0.09 \end{array}$$
$$\begin{array}{r} 0.45 \\ 0.86 \\ + 0.76 \end{array}$$
$$\begin{array}{r} 0.99 \\ 0.83 \\ + 0.76 \end{array}$$
$$\begin{array}{r} 0.45 \\ 0.93 \\ + 0.62 \end{array}$$
$$\begin{array}{r} 0.87 \\ 0.85 \\ + 0.56 \end{array}$$

4.
$$\begin{array}{r} 0.606 \\ 0.006 \\ + 0.600 \end{array}$$
$$\begin{array}{r} 0.3 \\ 0.03 \\ + 0.009 \end{array}$$
$$\begin{array}{r} 0.45 \\ 0.04 \\ + 0.054 \end{array}$$
$$\begin{array}{r} 0.09 \\ 0.905 \\ + 0.005 \end{array}$$
$$\begin{array}{r} 0.874 \\ 0.84 \\ + 0.4 \end{array}$$

5.
$$\begin{array}{r} 2.3 \\ 0.3 \\ + 0.04 \end{array}$$
$$\begin{array}{r} 9.25 \\ 9.2 \\ + 3.005 \end{array}$$
$$\begin{array}{r} 8.6 \\ 0.3 \\ + 2.4 \end{array}$$
$$\begin{array}{r} 5.30 \\ 0.05 \\ + 9 \end{array}$$
$$\begin{array}{r} 8.4 \\ 4.03 \\ + 0.006 \end{array}$$

6. 0.03 + 4.5 + 0.009 =

7. 9.05 + 44.6 + 8.05 =

8. 6.25 + 9.03 + 0.003 =

9. 4.52 + 9.7 + 3.002 =

10. 5.62 + 9.5 + 5.7 =

11. 8.6 + 3.27 + 0.04 =

12. 0.006 + 6.0 + 0.09 =

13. 9.3 + 4.56 + 0.05 =

Addition of dollars and cents:

Work Here

1. $0.02 + $6.35 + $0.59 =

2. $3.61 + $14.00 + $0.83 =

3. $3.42 + $0.61 + $2.98 + $8.75 =

4. $4.05 + $2.98 + $0.06 + $9.95 =

5. $40.87 + $6.53 + $0.06 + $5.43 + $6.25 =

6. $18.56 + $9.37 + $4.25 + $12.59 =

7. $8.39 + $105.26 + $4.25 + $16.30 + $4.30 =

8. $200.04 + $4.39 + $0.86 + $18.39 + $4.35 =

9. $49.36 + $14.92 + $0.03 + $16.52 + $306.56 =

10. $29.45 + 8.56 + $39.64 + $87.42 + $39.95 =

11. $140.56 + $89.95 + $56.87 + $32.52 + $39.95

12. $14.25 + $59.36 + $24.86 + $29.95 + $3.06 =

Use decimals to solve the following:

Example: $4\frac{1}{2} + 6\frac{1}{4} + 8\frac{1}{3} = 19.083$

$$4\frac{1}{2} = 4.5$$

$$6\frac{1}{4} = 6.25$$

$$8\frac{1}{3} = 8.333$$

$$\begin{array}{r} 4.5 \\ 6.25 \\ +\ 8.333 \\ \hline 19.083 \end{array}$$

1. $8\frac{1}{2} + 3\frac{1}{4} =$

2. $9.5 + 6\frac{1}{3} =$

3. $9.005 + 6\frac{1}{8} + 3 =$

4. $2\frac{1}{5} + 9\frac{1}{4} + 6\frac{2}{5} =$

5. $8\frac{7}{8} + 3\frac{1}{4} + 2\frac{1}{2} + 3.5 =$

6. $0.006 + 8\frac{1}{4} + 6 =$

7. $5.4 + 9\frac{1}{3} + 18\frac{3}{4} =$

8. $4\frac{7}{8} + 6.44 + 9.6 + 8\frac{1}{4} =$

9. $3\frac{5}{8} + 2\frac{1}{4} + 18\frac{4}{5} + 20.05 =$

10. $13\frac{1}{3} + 4\frac{1}{4} + 3.64 + 0.003 =$

11. $19\frac{1}{8} + 4\frac{3}{4} + 0.06 + 9.4 =$

12. $5\frac{3}{5} + 19\frac{2}{3} + 8\frac{1}{5} + 2\frac{1}{8} =$

13. $6.4 + 9.56 + 0.06 + 8\frac{7}{8} =$

14. $14.5 + 190.06 + 8\frac{4}{5} + 5\frac{7}{8} =$

Subtraction of Decimals

When subtracting decimals keep the decimal point in the subtrahend and the decimal point in the minuend directly under each other. Remember, you may drop the zeros when the answer ends in zeros.

Example 1: 3.62 − 1.41 = 2.21

$$\begin{array}{r} 3.62 \\ -\ 1.41 \\ \hline 2.21 \end{array}$$

Example 2: 19.36 − 4.86 = 14.50 or 14.5

$$\begin{array}{r} 19.36 \\ -\ 4.86 \\ \hline 14.50 \ \text{or} \ 14.5 \end{array}$$

Subract.

1.
$$\begin{array}{r} 0.3 \\ -\ 0.2 \end{array}$$
$$\begin{array}{r} 0.67 \\ -\ 0.52 \end{array}$$
$$\begin{array}{r} 0.039 \\ -\ 0.022 \end{array}$$
$$\begin{array}{r} 0.45 \\ -\ 0.16 \end{array}$$
$$\begin{array}{r} 8.6 \\ -\ 4.2 \end{array}$$

2.
$$\begin{array}{r} 5.67 \\ -\ 2.91 \end{array}$$
$$\begin{array}{r} 13.66 \\ -\ 2.55 \end{array}$$
$$\begin{array}{r} 18.4 \\ -\ 6.3 \end{array}$$
$$\begin{array}{r} 24.603 \\ -\ 12.401 \end{array}$$
$$\begin{array}{r} 2.303 \\ -\ 1.202 \end{array}$$

3.
$$\begin{array}{r} 3.049 \\ -\ 2.015 \end{array}$$
$$\begin{array}{r} 1.006 \\ -\ 0.515 \end{array}$$
$$\begin{array}{r} 8.325 \\ -\ 0.059 \end{array}$$
$$\begin{array}{r} 0.25 \\ -\ 0.09 \end{array}$$
$$\begin{array}{r} 3.67 \\ -\ 1.79 \end{array}$$

4.
$$\begin{array}{r} 4.3 \\ -\ 0.9 \end{array}$$
$$\begin{array}{r} 8.6 \\ -\ 0.5 \end{array}$$
$$\begin{array}{r} 2.005 \\ -\ 0.9 \end{array}$$
$$\begin{array}{r} 14.56 \\ -\ 0.96 \end{array}$$
$$\begin{array}{r} 8.65 \\ -\ 0.09 \end{array}$$

5.
$$\begin{array}{r} 8 \\ -\ 4.6 \end{array}$$
$$\begin{array}{r} 12 \\ -\ 0.06 \end{array}$$
$$\begin{array}{r} 14 \\ -\ 0.395 \end{array}$$
$$\begin{array}{r} 4 \\ -\ 0.06 \end{array}$$
$$\begin{array}{r} 0.4 \\ -\ 0.009 \end{array}$$

6.
$$\begin{array}{r} 1.6 \\ -\ 0.9 \end{array}$$
$$\begin{array}{r} 2.5 \\ -\ 0.8 \end{array}$$
$$\begin{array}{r} 13.675 \\ -\ 1.926 \end{array}$$
$$\begin{array}{r} 4.837 \\ -\ 1.933 \end{array}$$
$$\begin{array}{r} 4.685 \\ -\ 2.519 \end{array}$$

7.
$$\begin{array}{r} \$9.46 \\ -\ 1.39 \end{array} \qquad \begin{array}{r} \$3.56 \\ -\ 2.98 \end{array} \qquad \begin{array}{r} \$14.56 \\ -\ 2.39 \end{array} \qquad \begin{array}{r} \$18.39 \\ -\ 14.35 \end{array} \qquad \begin{array}{r} \$2.69 \\ -\ 1.06 \end{array}$$

8.
$$\begin{array}{r} \$12.56 \\ -\ 3.97 \end{array} \qquad \begin{array}{r} \$4.89 \\ -\ 0.96 \end{array} \qquad \begin{array}{r} \$14.00 \\ -\ 3.98 \end{array} \qquad \begin{array}{r} \$4.50 \\ -\ 1.99 \end{array} \qquad \begin{array}{r} \$15.00 \\ -\ 7.39 \end{array}$$

9. $4.63 - 0.59 =$

10. $13.54 - 4.36 =$

11. $2.003 - 0.5 =$

12. $9.05 - 0.09 =$

13. $14 - 2.5 =$

14. $8.32 - 0.006 =$

15. $\$23.06 - 4.98 =$

16. $\$21.56 - 14.86 =$

17. $\$12.08 - \$4.56 =$

18. $\$21 - \$4.98 =$

Use decimals to calculate the following:

Change the fractions to decimals and calculate.

Example: $6\frac{1}{2} - 1.4 = 5.1$

$\qquad 6.5$
$\underline{-1.4}$
$\qquad 5.1$

1. $6.55 - \frac{3}{4} =$

2. $12\frac{7}{8} - 2.06 =$

3. $4\frac{1}{4} - 3\frac{1}{2} =$

4. $6.4 - 2\frac{1}{3} =$

5. $2.3 - \frac{1}{5} =$

6. $16\frac{4}{5} - 2.66 =$

7. $8\frac{3}{4} - 1.005 =$

8. $9.603 - \frac{2}{3} =$

9. $4.55 - 1\frac{1}{4} =$

10. $\frac{7}{8} - \frac{1}{4} =$

11. $4\frac{4}{5} - 1.3 =$

12. $8\frac{1}{4} - 2\frac{1}{3} =$

13. $\frac{6}{9} - 0.45 =$

14. $14.3 - 1\frac{1}{4} =$

15. $2.006 - \frac{4}{5} =$

16. $3\frac{1}{3} - 2 =$

17. $16.009 - 14 =$

18. $5\frac{7}{8} - 2 =$

19. $15.009 - 7.3 =$

20. $21 - 4\frac{1}{4} =$

Multiplication of Decimals

To multiply decimals write down the numbers and multiply as you would with whole numbers. Find the total number of decimal places in the multiplier and the multiplicand and count out an equal number of decimal places in the product.

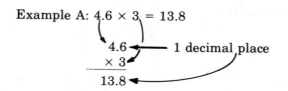

Example A: 4.6 × 3 = 13.8

```
  4.6  ←—— 1 decimal place
× 3
—————
 13.8
```

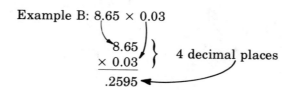

Example B: 8.65 × 0.03

```
  8.65  ⎫
× 0.03  ⎬  4 decimal places
—————
 .2595
```

Add zeros in your answer when necessary.

Example C: 0.09 × 0.003

```
  0.09   ⎫
× 0.003  ⎬  5 decimal places
————————
0.00027
```

Multiply.

1.

9	3	8	5	7
× 0.4	× 0.6	× 0.7	× 0.9	× 0.4

2.

0.93	4	0.805	6	0.84
× 8	× 0.67	× 9	× 0.69	× 5

3.

3.94	8.67	5.32	9.26	5.73
× 0.4	× 0.6	× 0.7	× 0.8	× 0.4

4.

4.03	16.09	32.56	4.006	9.03
× 0.4	× 0.9	× 0.05	× 0.4	× 0.04

5.	8.3 × 9.4	6.5 × 5.65	9.03 × 4.53	17.63 × 0.06	23.40 × 0.05

6.	36.05 × 0.29	8.467 × 0.063	45.9 × 0.006	5.325 × 3.2	9.672 × 0.009

7.	54 × 0.069	867 × 0.63	589.6 × 2.4	8.673 × 0.09	5.864 × 0.202

Multiplication of dollars and cents:

1.	$0.39 × 4	$0.56 × 3	$0.93 × 2	$0.87 × 5	$45 × 6

2.	$2.56 × 5	$3.95 × 4	$6.75 × 3	$8.45 × 6	$6.52 × 2

3.	$3.06 × 9	$30.09 × 8	$15.05 × 6	$4.00 × 5	$9.05 × 4

4.	$9.43 × 0.52	$91.46 × 0.25	$32.06 × 0.52	$46.52 × 0.67	$90.05 × 0.35

5.	$40.50 × 0.04	$30.60 × 0.06	$20.59 × 0.09	$39.99 × 0.004	$43.26 × 0.006

6.	$3.67 × 3.5	$9.45 × 6.2	$8.67 × 5.3	$9.98 × 9.2	$4.97 × 4.7

7.	$361.59 × 0.5	$247.82 × 0.67	$156.93 × 0.83	$187.26 × 9.5	$489.52 × 3.7

Calculate the following using decimals. Round off all answers to the nearest cent.

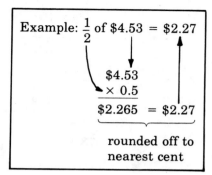

Example: $\frac{1}{2}$ of $4.53 = $2.27

$4.53
× 0.5
$2.265 = $2.27

rounded off to
nearest cent

Work Here

1. $\frac{1}{2}$ of $3.96 =

2. $\frac{1}{2}$ of $10.05 =

3. $\frac{3}{4}$ of $47.50 =

4. $6\frac{1}{2}$ of $3.97 =

5. $\frac{1}{8}$ of $49.95 =

6. $\frac{2}{3}$ of $99.99 =

7. $4\frac{2}{5}$ of $3.29 =

8. $\frac{3}{4}$ of $0.58 =

9. $2\frac{1}{4}$ of $4.87 =

10. $3\frac{1}{4}$ of $16.56 =

Find the cost of the following. Round off to the nearest cent.

Work Here

1. 5 kg of potatoes at $0.23/kg =

2. 6 m of cloth at $4.59/m =

3. 3 doz. eggs at 92 cents/dozen =

4. $2\frac{1}{4}$ kg of meat at $2.79/kg =

5. 15.5 square metres of carpet at $8.95 per square metre =

6. 15.5 L of gasoline at 24.9¢/L =

7. 19 m of wood trim at $1.59/m =

8. 24 cans of peas at $0.47 =

9. 13.5 square metres of linoleum at $7.50 per square metre =

10. 6.75 kg leg of lamb at $2.49/kg =

111

Division of Decimals

If the Divisor is a Whole Number

Study the example below.

$$\begin{array}{r} 6.82 \text{ R:5} \\ 9\overline{)61.43} \\ 54 \\ \hline 7\,4 \\ 7\,2 \\ \hline 23 \\ 18 \\ \hline 5 \end{array}$$

A. Write down the question.
B. Place the decimal point for the quotient directly above that of the dividend.
C. Divide as you would with whole numbers.

Divide the following.

1. $3\overline{)4.6}$ $5\overline{)9.36}$ $5\overline{)8.43}$ $6\overline{)9.675}$

2. $6\overline{)39.6}$ $4\overline{)4.006}$ $8\overline{)8.463}$ $9\overline{)9.673}$

3. $8\overline{)36.59}$ $9\overline{)867.62}$ $6\overline{).059}$ $4\overline{)3.695}$

4. $3\overline{)4.678}$ $6\overline{)4.093}$ $7\overline{)8.627}$ $9\overline{)7.326}$

5. $24\overline{)63.97}$ $27\overline{)386.452}$ $73\overline{)86.5943}$ $62\overline{)6.8727}$

If the Divisor is a Decimal

Study the example below.

$$.3\overline{)4.639}$$

A   B

A. Move the decimal point in the divisor to make a whole number.

B. Move the decimal point in the dividend the same number of places to the right as you moved it in the divisor.

The question now looks like this:

$$3\overline{)46.39}$$

and the solution is:

C
$$\begin{cases} 3\overline{)46.39} \end{cases} \quad 15.46 \text{ R:1}$$

D
$$\begin{cases} 3 \\ 16 \\ 15 \\ 1\,3 \\ 1\,2 \\ 19 \\ 18 \\ 1 \end{cases}$$

C. Place the decimal point for the quotient directly above the new decimal point in the dividend.

D. Divide as you would with whole numbers.

---

1. $.6\overline{)6.73}$ $.9\overline{).935}$ $.3\overline{)36.506}$ $.4\overline{).6257}$

2. $.9\overline{)8.667}$ $.8\overline{).0379}$ $.6\overline{)4.5675}$ $.5\overline{).4993}$

3. $.03\overline{).8367}$ $.04\overline{)9.6457}$ $.07\overline{)7.3467}$ $.09\overline{)2.4859}$

4. $.35\overline{)3.6794}$ $.62\overline{).00326}$ $.83\overline{).04975}$ $.64\overline{)8.4235}$

Divide (change the fractions to decimals):

1. $9.673 \div 7 =$

2. $8.403 \div 9 =$

3. $31.54 \div .3 =$

4. $9\frac{7}{8} \div 4 =$

5. $18\frac{1}{3} \div 3 =$

6. $5.067 \div .03 =$

7. $5\frac{1}{4} \div \frac{2}{5} =$

8. $14.679 \div .03 =$

9. $.06 \div \frac{4}{5} =$

10. $6.379 \div 2\frac{1}{4} =$

Calculate the cost of the following. Round off to the nearest cent.

Work Here

1. 1 can of peas if 6 cost $2.43 =

2. Bread costs 4 for $1.79. One loaf costs _____.

3. 5 kg of potatoes costs $1.85. One kg would cost _____.

4. Seven office chairs cost $472.50. One chair costs _____.

5. One hundred forty-four pencils cost $14.40. Twelve pencils cost _____.

6. Find the cost of 1 if 6 cost $8.95.

7. A car travelled 493 km on 20.5 L of gas. How many km does the car travel on one litre?

114

Test Your Skill

1. Round off to the nearest tenth.

0.34 =	9.25 =	9.35 =
0.67 =	3.61 =	16.05 =
8.453 =	5.26 =	18.11 =
5.673 =	3.976 =	23.456 =

2. Round off to the nearest cent.

$0.564 =	$ 9.645 =	$ 3.699 =
$0.391 =	$10.452 =	$ 4.675 =
$0.429 =	$16.429 =	$18.269 =
$0.316 =	$ 4.459 =	$ 4.562 =

3. Change these fractions to decimals.

$\frac{1}{2} =$	$\frac{1}{4} =$	$\frac{2}{5} =$	$2\frac{1}{8} =$	$8\frac{1}{9} =$
$\frac{1}{3} =$	$\frac{3}{4} =$	$\frac{3}{5} =$	$3\frac{1}{4} =$	$16\frac{7}{8} =$
$\frac{2}{3} =$	$\frac{1}{5} =$	$\frac{4}{5} =$	$9\frac{1}{4} =$	$14\frac{2}{3} =$

4. Circle the larger of the two.

8.9 or $8\frac{1}{3}$	9.6 or $9\frac{1}{2}$
$\frac{3}{4}$ or 0.74	$3\frac{1}{3}$ or $3\frac{1}{4}$
0.06 or 0.6	2.25 or $2\frac{1}{3}$
2.6 or 2.62	0.005 or 0.05

5. Circle the smaller of the two.

6.3 or $6\frac{1}{3}$	5.67 or 5.6
5.4 or 5.04	3.95 or 9.4
9.23 or $9\frac{1}{5}$	$2\frac{1}{4}$ or 2.3
6.5 or $6\frac{3}{4}$	$8\frac{7}{8}$ or 8.6

6. Add:

0.42	2.64	9.42	9.33	$3.65	$4.65
+ 0.6	+ 0.03	2.003	8.45	9.02	9.38
		+ 4.5	+ 0.005	+ 5.53	+ 8.45
					+ 6.45

7. Subtract:

2.04	8.67	6.003	$8.45	$4.59	18.56
− 1.02	− 3.94	− 2.5	− 5.21	− 3.26	− 2.99

8. Multiply:

0.4	3.6	8.45	6.56	$4.96	$16.39
× 2	× 5	× 0.02	× 3.2	× 8	× 4.5

$61.59	$4.62	$5.94	$36.26	$19.67	$187.59
× 45	× 0.003	× 0.07	× 3.6	× 6.3	× 6.7

9. Divide:

3)9.65   2)0.4763   0.03)3.6594   1.8)363.496

2)$19.56   6)$23.56   9)$875.46   18)$1365.47

Calculate the following:

(a) $9\frac{1}{4} \times 3.5 =$

(b) $\frac{1}{2}$ of $4.96 =

(c) $3.6 + 4.62 =$

(d) Find the sum of 3.65 and 9.673.

(e) Divide 4.673 by 9.

(f) $\frac{1}{3} + 2\frac{1}{4} + 6\frac{1}{3} + 4.6 =$

(g) Find $\frac{7}{8}$ of $6.98 to the nearest cent.

(h) Find the difference between $6.42 and $3.59.

(i) Find $\frac{1}{4}$ of $8.69.

(j) Divide $9.65 by 3.7.

CHAPTER FOUR
PER CENT

The Meaning of Per Cent

1. How many squares are in the chart? _____

2. How could you express $\dfrac{35}{100}$ on the chart? _____

   _____

3. How could 0.35 be expressed on the chart? _____

   _____

4. Per cent or % means *out of one hundred*.
   Therefore 35% means *35 out of 100*.

   $\dfrac{35}{100}$ and 0.35 and 35% all mean the same quantity.

Express as a per cent:

$\dfrac{36}{100} =$ $\qquad$ $\dfrac{90}{100} =$

$\dfrac{93}{100} =$ $\qquad$ $\dfrac{65}{100} =$

$\dfrac{4}{100} =$ $\qquad$ $\dfrac{16}{100} =$

$\dfrac{6}{100} =$ $\qquad$ $\dfrac{82}{100} =$

$\dfrac{15}{100} =$ $\qquad$ $\dfrac{14}{100} =$

Express as a per cent:

0.62 = $\qquad$ 0.09 =

0.59 = $\qquad$ 0.63 =

0.06 = $\qquad$ 0.87 =

0.35 = $\qquad$ 0.45 =

0.99 = $\qquad$ 0.62 =

Changing a Per Cent to a Decimal Fraction

To change a per cent to a decimal fraction drop the "%" and move the decimal point 2 places to the *left*.

Example:

$$46\% = 0.46 \qquad\qquad 4.5\% = 0.045$$
$$2\% = 0.02 \qquad\qquad 19\frac{1}{4}\% = 0.1925$$
$$123\% = 1.23 \qquad\qquad 5\frac{1}{2}\% = 0.055$$

Note: In changing a *fractional* per cent (for example, 19¼%) to a decimal, change it first to a decimal per cent (19.25%), and then to a decimal fraction by moving the decimal 2 places left.

Change to decimal fractions:

(a) 6% =   (b) 12% =   (c) 40% =   (d) 135% =

9% =   14% =   93% =   923% =

8% =   18% =   50% =   425% =

7% =   37% =   70% =   162% =

3% =   42% =   52% =   196% =

(e) 290% =   (f) 32.6% =   (g) $2\frac{1}{4}\%$ =   (h) 0.7% =

350% =   92.5% = $8\frac{1}{5}\%$ = $\frac{1}{4}\%$ =

620% =   24.5% = $6\frac{7}{8}\%$ =   0.03% =

940% =   93.6% = $5\frac{3}{4}\%$ = $\frac{3}{4}\%$ =

475% =   20.6% = $9\frac{4}{5}\%$ =   0.09% =

Changing a Decimal Fraction to a Per Cent

To change a decimal fraction to a per cent move the decimal point two places *right* and add "%."

Examples:

$$0.25 = 25\%$$
$$0.06 = 6\%$$
$$2.5 = 250\%$$

$$0.6 = 60\%$$
$$3.9 = 390\%$$
$$0.006 = 0.6\%$$

Note: When you change a decimal to a per cent you must sometimes add zeros so you can move the decimal 2 places right (0.2 = 20% or 2.3 = 230%).

Change to per cents:

(a) 0.35 =   (b) 0.06 =   (c) 0.4 =   (d) 2.64 =

0.64 =   0.09 =   0.6 =   8.65 =

0.92 =   0.04 =   0.9 =   9.35 =

0.87 =   0.08 =   0.3 =   7.63 =

0.56 =   0.05 =   0.5 =   8.44 =

(e) 0.025 =   (f) 1 =   (g) 0.125 =   (h) 3.05 =

0.097 =   3 =   0.637 =   5.35 =

0.836 =   6 =   0.845 =   9.003 =

0.452 =   7 =   0.325 =   4.2 =

0.693 =   5 =   0.957 =   5.6 =

Changing a Common Fraction to a Per Cent

To change a common fraction to a per cent change it first to a decimal fraction and then change the decimal fraction to a per cent.

Examples:

$$\frac{1}{4} = 0.25 = 25\%$$

$$\frac{7}{8} = 0.875 = 87\ \%$$

$$2\frac{1}{2} = 2.5 = 250\%$$

(a) $\frac{1}{4} =$

$\frac{3}{4} =$

$\frac{1}{5} =$

$\frac{2}{5} =$

$\frac{3}{8} =$

(b) $\frac{3}{10} =$

$\frac{4}{10} =$

$\frac{5}{50} =$

$\frac{9}{100} =$

$\frac{11}{100} =$

(c) $2\frac{1}{4} =$

$3\frac{1}{5} =$

$6\frac{2}{3} =$

$8\frac{3}{5} =$

$7\frac{4}{5} =$

(d) $\frac{1}{6} =$

$\frac{1}{7} =$

$\frac{3}{5} =$

$\frac{3}{7} =$

$\frac{5}{7} =$

(e) $\frac{6}{8} =$

$\frac{7}{12} =$

$\frac{9}{10} =$

$\frac{8}{10} =$

$\frac{7}{8} =$

(f) $2\frac{1}{6} =$

$18\frac{2}{3} =$

$16\frac{1}{7} =$

$19\frac{4}{5} =$

$36\frac{1}{8} =$

(g) $\frac{1}{100} =$

$\frac{3}{100} =$

$\frac{36}{100} =$

$\frac{45}{100} =$

$\frac{93}{100} =$

(h) $\frac{1}{16} =$

$\frac{3}{50} =$

$\frac{6}{75} =$

$\frac{9}{25} =$

$\frac{19}{50} =$

Fill in the blanks:

%	Decimal	Fraction
50%	0.5	$\frac{1}{2}$
—	0.25	—
75%	—	—
—	0.8	—
—	—	$\frac{3}{5}$
12.5%	—	—
—	—	$3\frac{1}{3}$
—	0.2	—
100%	—	—
—	—	$\frac{1}{8}$
—	0.85	—

%	Decimal	Fraction
—	0.9	—
125%	—	—
—	—	$2\frac{3}{4}$
—	1.3	—
200%	—	—
—	0.65	—
—	—	$\frac{3}{8}$
10%	—	—
—	—	$\frac{8}{100}$
93%	—	—
—	0.75	—

Circle the largest.

1. 2% or 0.22 or $\frac{2}{100}$

2. 1% or $\frac{1}{10}$ or $\frac{1}{100}$

3. 0.66 or 60% or $\frac{60}{100}$

4. $\frac{14}{100}$ or $\frac{14}{60}$ or 14%

5. $\frac{4}{5}$ or 0.91 or 90%

6. $\frac{1}{2}$ or $\frac{1}{9}$ or 0.76

7. 0.4 or 42% or $\frac{4}{10}$

8. $\frac{2}{3}$ or 66% or 0.669

9. $\frac{1}{2}$ or 52% or $\frac{5}{10}$

10. $1\frac{1}{2}$ or 150% or $1\frac{1}{3}$

Circle the smallest.

1. 0.2 or 0.3 or 0.02

2. 20% or 13% or 125%

3. $\frac{1}{3}$ or 0.3 or 31%

4. $\frac{6}{10}$ or 62% or 0.63

5. 0.23 or 23% or $\frac{1}{5}$

6. 0.6 or 61% or $\frac{4}{5}$

7. $\frac{1}{7}$ or 16% or 4%

8. 0.9 or 9% or $\frac{9}{10}$

9. $\frac{2}{3}$ or $\frac{3}{5}$ or 59%

10. 0.6 or $\frac{6}{10}$ or $\frac{1}{5}$

Finding a Certain Per Cent of a Number

To find a certain per cent of a number change the per cent to a decimal and multiply.

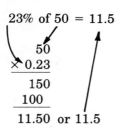

$$23\% \text{ of } 50 = 11.5$$

$$
\begin{array}{r}
50 \\
\times\, 0.23 \\
\hline
150 \\
100 \\
\hline
11.50 \text{ or } 11.5
\end{array}
$$

$$3\% \text{ of } 450 = 13.5$$

$$
\begin{array}{r}
450 \\
\times\, 0.03 \\
\hline
13.50 \text{ or } 13.5
\end{array}
$$

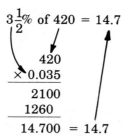

$$3\tfrac{1}{2}\% \text{ of } 420 = 14.7$$

$$
\begin{array}{r}
420 \\
\times\, 0.035 \\
\hline
2100 \\
1260 \\
\hline
14.700 = 14.7
\end{array}
$$

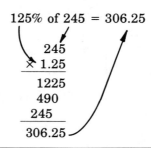

$$125\% \text{ of } 245 = 306.25$$

$$
\begin{array}{r}
245 \\
\times\, 1.25 \\
\hline
1225 \\
490 \\
245 \\
\hline
306.25
\end{array}
$$

Calculate:

1. 22% of 30 =

2. 92% of 125 =

3. 81% of 46 =

4. 32% of 56 =

5. 42% of 130 =

6. 90% of 70 =

7. 32% of 57 =

8. 6% of 93 =

Work Here

9. 9% of 67 =

10. 5% of 83 =

11. 8% of 26 =

12. 2% of 36 =

13. 4% of 54 =

14. $6\frac{1}{2}$% of 87 =

15. $2\frac{1}{4}$% of 92 =

16. $8\frac{1}{3}$% of 73 =

17. $9\frac{3}{4}$% of 83 =

18. $2\frac{1}{5}$% of 54%

19. $6\frac{1}{8}$% of 325 =

20. $2\frac{2}{3}$% of 124 =

21. $7\frac{3}{5}$% of 846 =

22. 130% of 721 =

23. 250% of 836 =

24. 120% of 245 =

25. 7% of $12.56

26. 7% of $9.37

27. 8% of $8.56

28. 9% of $17.36

29. 25% of $56.50

30. $\frac{1}{4}$% of $923.30

31. $\frac{1}{3}$% of $637.50

32. $\frac{7}{8}$% of $873.30

33. $4\frac{1}{2}$% of $87.56

34. 9% of $93.56

35. $8\frac{1}{2}$% of $16.93

36. 5.5% of $43.50

37. 9.2% of $26.90

38. 6.7% of $47.80

39. $3\frac{1}{4}$% of $23.30

40. 6.75% of $37.80

Calculate the Sales Tax and the Total Cost on the following items.

Purchase	7% Sales Tax on All Items (Work Here)	Tax	Total Cost
$ 9.95			
$ 18.50			
$125.30			
$ 46.50			
$246.50			
$ 93.99			
$ 46.50			
$ 87.95			
$ 93.37			
$ 47.50			

Calculate the discount on the following purchases.

Regular Price	$29.95	$56.95	$27.50	$18.95	$53.60	$3.95	$9.95
Discount	20%	30%	10%	25%	50%	10%	20%
Sale Price							

Salesmen often sell on commission. Find the commission for the following sales.

Sale	Rate of Commission	Commission	Sale	Rate of Commission	Commission
$ 320.00	6%		$ 950.00	8%	
$ 495.00	3%		$3240.00	10%	
$4250.00	5%		$2650.00	5%	
$ 680.00	2%		$ 825.00	25%	
$ 380.00	7%		$ 999.95	10%	

Finding Simple Interest on a Loan

If you borrow money, you must pay *interest* to the person lending to you. Interest is stated as a per cent called the *rate*. You pay interest for the *time* you borrow the money. The amount you borrow is called the *principal*.

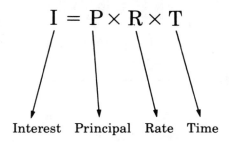

$$I = P \times R \times T$$

Interest   Principal   Rate   Time

Example:

John borrowed $500 at a 15% interest rate for 3 years. How much interest must he pay?

I = P × R × T	A. Write the formula.
I = $500.00 × 15% × 3 years	B. Fill in the numbers.
I = $500.00 × 0.15 × 3	C. Change the % to a decimal.
I = $75.00 × 3	D. Calculate the value of I.
I = $225.00	

John had to pay $225.00 interest for a loan of $500 for 3 years.

Calculate the simple interest for the following loans.

Principal	Rate	Time	Interest
$ 700.00	12%	1 yr.	
$1300.00	15%	2 yrs.	
$ 750.00	12%	1 yr.	
$1600.00	20%	2 yrs.	
$ 900.00	11%	5 yrs.	
$ 780.00	23%	2 yrs.	
$3000.00	18%	3 yrs.	
$4200.00	16%	3 yrs.	
$2250.00	18%	2 yrs.	
$ 180.00	12%	6 yrs.	

PANTS

regular

$25.00 to $40.00

25% off

DRESSES

. . . .

Reg. $19.95 to $29.95

20% off

TOYS

33% off

RINGS, WALLETS, PURSES

ALL REDUCED 15%

SCARFS and TIES all 35% off

SHIRTS Reg. $9.95 to $19.95

15% to 30% off

A store had a special sale and items were reduced in price.

Regular Price	Rate of Discount	Amount of Discount	Sale Price	Work Here
Shirt $9.95	15%			
Tie $5.95	35%			
Dress $29.95	20%			
Wallet $12.95	15%			
Pants $35.00	25%			
Games (Toys) $4.95 $3.50 $4.75	33% 33% 33%			
Shirt $16.95	25%			
Pants $25.95	25%			
Purse $29.00	15%			
Dress $24.95	20%			
Scarf $4.99	35%			

128

Finding What Per Cent One Number is of Another

To find what per cent one number is of another study the examples below.

1. 2 is what per cent of 4?

$$\frac{2}{4} = \frac{1}{2} = 0.5 = 50\%$$

2 is 50% of 4

2. 6 is what per cent of 8?

$$\frac{6}{8} = \frac{3}{4} = 0.75 = 75\%$$

6 is 75% of 8

A. Make a fraction to express what fraction one number is of another.
B. Reduce the fraction to lowest terms (if necessary).
C. Change the fraction to a decimal.
D. Change the decimal to a per cent.

Calculate:

Work Here

1. 3 is _____ % of 5.

2. 2 is _____ % of 3.

3. 6 is _____ % of 9.

4. 9 is _____ % of 10.

5. 4 is _____ % of 20.

6. 2 is _____ % of 5.

7. 7 is _____ % of 28.

8. 6 is _____ % of 30.

9. 10 is _____ % of 100.

10. 5 is _____ % of 40.

For another way of asking the same question see the sample below.

---

6 is _____ % of 24.
or
What per cent of 24 is 6?
or
What % of 24 is 6?

Calculate the following:

Work Here

1. 3 is _____ % of 12.

2. What % of 12 is 2?

3. What percent of 9 is 5?

4. 12 is _____ % of 60.

5. 9 is _____ % of 45.

6. 18 is _____ % of 90.

7. What % of 24 is 3?

8. What per cent of 30 is 5?

9. 40 is _____ % of 120.

10. What % of 30 is 16?

11. 8 is _____ % of 72.

12. What % of 16 is 5?

13. 9 is _____ % of 81.

14. What per cent of 61 is 5?

15. 7 is _____ % of 40.

Finding 100% of a Number When Another Per Cent of It is Known

15% of what number is 45?

15% is = 45

$1\% \text{ is} = \dfrac{45}{15} = 3$

A. State the given information in the form of an equivalance, as shown.
B. Find 1%.

100% is = 300

C. Multiply the 1% by 100 to find the whole number.

Solution:

15% of 300 is 45.

Calculate:

Work Here

1. 50% of _____ = 30

2. 25% of _____ = 100

3. 30% of _____ = 90

4. 75% of _____ = 75

5. 90% of _____ = 270

6. 60% of _____ = 120

7. 8% of _____ = 72

8. 12% of _____ = 36

9. 15% of _____ = 75

10. 20% of _____ = 25

Below are different ways of asking the same question.

> 60% of _____ = 120
> or
> 60% of what number is 120?
> or
> 120 is 60% of what number?

Calculate:

Work Here

1. 16% of _____ = 40

2. 45% of what number is 40?

3. 32 is 50% of what number?

4. 60% of what number is 240?

5. 80% of _____ = 480

6. 25% of _____ = 60

7. 96 is 10% of what number?

8. 16% of what number is 60?

9. 90 is 30% of what number?

10. 4% of _____ = 60

11. 9 is 3% of what number?

12. 4 is 9% of _____.

Situation Solving

1. A salesman sold $2345.00 to his customers on a 1-day trip. His company pays him a 4% commission on all sales. How much did he earn?

2. Find the sales tax on a $540.00 purchase if the sales tax is 7%.

3. Joan saves $50.00 of her salary each month. Her monthly pay is $250. What percent of her pay does she save?

4. A refrigerator cost a dealer $380.00. If he wishes to make a 20% profit, how much must he charge a customer who buys the refrigerator?

5. An item was on sale for $24.00. The sign said that the sale price was a 25% reduction from the regular price. How much was the item before it went on sale?

6. A secretary for a company earns $230.00 weekly. If the secretary got a 10% raise, how much raise did she get? How much will her new salary be?

7. On sales of $700.00 a salesman earned $40.00. What is his rate of commission?

Situation Solving

8. A house is sold for $78 500.00 and the salesperson got a 6% commission. How much did the salesperson earn?

9. A family borrowed $900.00 for 1 year and had to pay $120.00 interest. What rate of interest was charged on the loan?

10. A salesman sold 6 suits at $150.00 each. If he gets a 4% commission on all that he sells, how much did he earn?

11. Your electric bill is $43.60. If you get a 3% discount for paying early, how much do you save by paying early? How much will the bill be if you pay early?

12. A student can save money by buying school supplies during the off season. If you save $4.00 on a $24.00 purchase, what is your rate of discount?

13. Find the 7% sales tax and total price on the following items.

	Tax	Cost
(a) Shirt—$9.95	_____	_____
(b) Trousers—$49.50	_____	_____
(c) Skirt—$29.99	_____	_____

14. A customer bought an item at a 25%-off sale. If the sale price is $40.00, what is the regular price?

134

Test Your Skill

1. Change to decimals:

(a) $60\% =$

(b) $20\% =$

(c) $45\% =$

(d) $9\% =$

(e) $8\% =$

(f) $3\% =$

(g) $3\frac{1}{2}\% =$

(h) $2\frac{1}{4}\% =$

(i) $15\frac{1}{2}\% =$

(j) $100\% =$

(k) $300\% =$

(l) $500\% =$

(m) $9.5\% =$

(n) $16.25\% =$

(o) $23\frac{1}{3}\% =$

2. Change to %:

(a) $0.25 =$

(b) $0.43 =$

(c) $2.5 =$

(d) $0.4 =$

(e) $0.6 =$

(f) $\frac{1}{2} =$

(g) $\frac{3}{4} =$

(h) $\frac{2}{3} =$

(i) $2\frac{1}{2} =$

(j) $\frac{1}{5} =$

(k) $2\frac{1}{3} =$

(l) $6\frac{1}{4} =$

(m) $0.325 =$

(n) $0.675 =$

(o) $0.8 =$

3. Calculate:

(a) 16% of $45 =$

(b) $2\frac{1}{2}\%$ of $325 =$

(c) 25% of $93 =$

(d) Find 6% of $\$87.00 =$

(e) 12% of $\$90.00 =$

(f) $13\frac{1}{2}\%$ of $\$420.00 =$

(g) Find 9% of 83.

(h) 25% of $30 =$

(i) Find 60% of $90 =$

(j) 125% of $47 =$

4. Calculate:

(a) 6 is _____ % of 9.

(b) 75% of what number is 25?

(c) 12 is what percent of 60?

(d) 6% of _____ is 48.

(e) 9 is _____ % of 81.

(f) What % of 16 is 5?

(g) 8% of _____ % is 72.

(h) 7 is _____ % of 49.

(i) 90 is 30% of what number?

(j) What per cent of 60 is 10?

5. A store had a sale. Fill in the chart to find the sale price.

Item	Regular Price	Reduced By	Savings	Sale Price
Shirt	$14.95	20%		
Skirt	$29.95	30%		
Scarf	$9.95	25%		
Purse	$18.95	15%		
Trousers	$39.95	20%		

6. Calculate the interest on the following loans:

Principal	Rate	Time	Interest	Amt. to Be Repayed
$ 500.00	18%	1 yr.		
$ 750.00	16%	2 yrs.		
$3250.00	14%	3 yrs.		
$5000.00	$11\frac{1}{4}$ %	5 yrs.		

7. Calculate sales tax on the following:

Price	Rate of Sales Tax	Amt. of Sales Tax	Cost of Item
$ 9.95	7%		
$100.00	5%		
$ 36.50	6%		
$ 79.95	7%		

CHAPTER FIVE
METRIC MEASUREMENT
(Système International or SI units)

Canada has entered a period of time when metric measurement has become increasingly popular. It is important that you "think metric." By learning how to measure length, mass and temperature in metric terms you will be able to use the system easily.

Length

The basic unit of length is the *metre*, which is approximately the distance from the tip of your nose to the end of your fingers. Other commonly used units are described below.

---

kilometre = 1000 metres

centimetre = $\frac{1}{100}$ of a metre—approximately the width of your little finger   Actual size: ⊢————⊣

millimetre = $\frac{1}{1000}$ of a metre = $\frac{1}{10}$ of a centimetre   Actual size: ⊢

As can be seen, in the metric system the names of units are formed by adding prefixes to the name of a basic unit. This is also true for the metric symbols. The symbol for "metre" is "m," and so we arrive at the following:

kilometre	km	centimetre	cm
metre	m	millimetre	mm

The chart below gives some commonly used metric prefixes, their symbols and their meanings. (They are not really abbreviations, and so they do not have a period after them.)

kilo-	hecto-	deca-	(*metre*)	deci-	centi-	milli-
k	h	da	(m)	d	c	m
1000 ×	100 ×	10 ×	—	$\times \frac{1}{10}$	$\times \frac{1}{100}$	$\times \frac{1}{1000}$

Look at a metre stick. Identify:

    1 m
    1 cm
    1 mm

Using what you have learned, consider in which unit of measurement you would express each of the following. Circle the correct answer.

1. The distance from Toronto to North Bay—km, m, cm, mm

2. Your height—km, mm, cm, m

3. The length of your living room—m, cm, mm

4. The length of a wood screw—m, cm, km, mm

5. The width of a wood screw—m, cm, km, mm

6. The height of a fence—mm, km, cm, m

7. The depth of a hem on a dress—m, cm, mm, km

8. The width of a precision gear in a watch—cm, mm, km, m

9. The distance to work if you drive—km, m, cm, mm

10. Cloth is sold by the—km, cm, mm, m

11. The setting of a spark plug—cm, km, mm, m

12. Running around a track once—m, mm, km, cm

13. A 4-day canoe trip—mm, m, km, cm

14. A trip across Canada—mm, cm, km, m

15. The height of a door—mm, km, m, cm

16. The thickness of a piece of tin—cm, mm, km, m

17. The height of the frame around a house window—cm, m, mm, km

18. The distance along the hall of a large school—cm, m, mm, km

19. The thickness of sheet metal for a car by micrometer—km, mm, m, cm

20. The width of a bed—mm, km, m, cm

The Metre

Hold a metre stick in your hands. Get an idea of the length of a metre. Have a friend hold his hands one metre apart. Measure to see how accurate the guess was.

How many cm in 1 m? _____
How many mm in 1 m? _____

With the metre stick in your hands estimate and then measure accurately the following to the nearest metre.

	Estimate	Actual Measurement
1. The length of a room	_____	_____
2. The width of the same room	_____	_____
3. The length of a school hall	_____	_____
4. The width of a school hall	_____	_____
5. The length of an athletic track	_____	_____
6. The length of a 2 × 4 stud	_____	_____
7. The height of a door	_____	_____
8. The length of a fence	_____	_____
9. The distance from your house to a neighbour's	_____	_____
10. The length of a car	_____	_____
11. The total length of six very long strides	_____	_____
12. The length of a sidewalk	_____	_____

The Centimetre (cm)

This is a centimetre ruler.

100 cm = 1 m

Measure these lines:

├─────	_____ cm
├────────────	_____ cm
├──────────────────	_____ cm
├────────────────────────	_____ cm
├────	_____ cm
├────────────────────────────	_____ cm
├────────────	_____ cm
├──────	_____ cm
├────────────────	_____ cm
├──────────	_____ cm

Estimate the length of the following, then measure accurately.

	Estimate	Actual Measurement
1. The width of a table	_____	_____
2. Your height	_____	_____
3. Your waist	_____	_____
4. Your finger span	_____	_____
5. A friend's height	_____	_____
6. The width of a small car	_____	_____
7. The width of a bolt of cloth	_____	_____
8. The width of a door	_____	_____
9. The length of a piece of wood	_____	_____
10. The length of this page	_____	_____

Measure these lines:

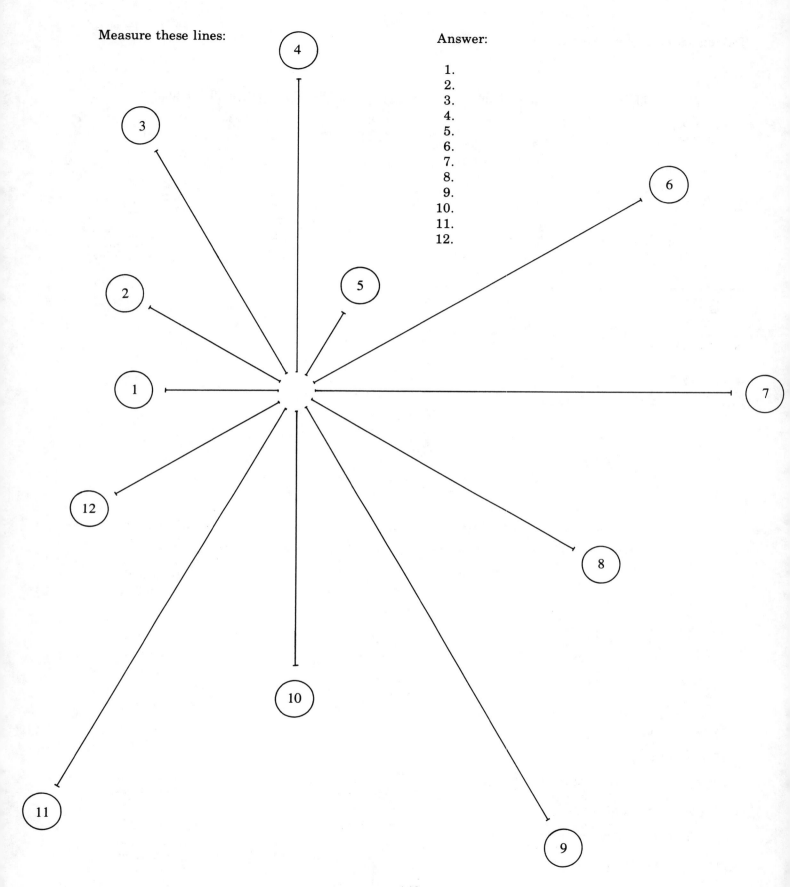

Answer:
1.
2.
3.
4.
5.
6.
7.
8.
9.
10.
11.
12.

Adding metric measurements:

1.

```
                                             19 m          83 m          7 m
                                              4 m          21 m         84 m
      7 m         3 m                       + 241 m         6 m         21 m
    + 6 m       + 4 m                                     + 9 m         13 m
                                                                      +  4 m
```

2.

```
                                            9m   6 cm        14 m   6 cm
                                           18 m  6 cm       118 m   9 cm
     1 m 3 cm        8 m 24 cm           +  9 m 40 cm         36 m 18 cm
   + 4 m 5 cm      + 2 m 31 cm                             + 87 m 35 cm
```

Now try these:

```
┌─────────────────────────────┐
│  Example:                   │
│                             │
│      1 m   90 cm            │
│    + 3 m   41 cm            │
│      4 m  131 cm            │
│                             │
│    = 5 m   31 cm            │
└─────────────────────────────┘
```

3.
```
      3 m 81 cm              14 m 36 cm              27 m 67 cm
    + 6 m 72 cm            +  5 m 97 cm            + 31 m 94 cm

    ____ m ____ cm          ____ m ____ cm          ____ m ____ cm
  = ____ m ____ cm        = ____ m ____ cm        = ____ m ____ cm
```

4.
```
      2 m 13 cm              16 m 89 cm               4 m 97 cm
     19 m 93 cm             187 m 39 cm              47 m 68 cm
   + 13 m 74 cm           + 20 m 86 cm            + 193 m 92 cm

    ____ m ____ cm          ____ m ____ cm          ____ m ____ cm
  = ____ m ____ cm        = ____ m ____ cm        = ____ m ____ cm
```

5.
```
     87 m 92 cm             121 m 92 cm              97 m 67 cm
     32 m 67 cm              56 m 76 cm              32 m 82 cm
    420 m 82 cm              48 m 67 cm             562 m 69 cm
   + 16 m 92 cm            + 90 m 83 cm            + 83 m 47 cm

    ____ m ____ cm          ____ m ____ cm          ____ m ____ cm
  = ____ m ____ cm        = ____ m ____ cm        = ____ m ____ cm
```

143

Subtracting metric measurements:

1.

3 m	14 m	82 cm	36 cm	183 cm
− 1 m	− 9 m	− 19 cm	− 20 cm	− 140 cm

2.

9 m 30 cm	26 m 87 cm	42 m 23 cm	92 m 16 cm
− 6 m 30 cm	− 9 m 28 cm	− 23 m 16 cm	− 83 m 9 cm

Now try these, using borrowing:

```
Example:

  6 m 20 cm   =     5 m 120 cm
− 3 m 32 cm       − 3 m   32 cm
                    2 m   88 cm
```

3.

9 m 36 cm	4 m 36 cm	6 m 47 cm
− 6 m 92 cm	− 2 m 82 cm	− 7 m 91 cm

4.

18 m 36 cm	36 m 2 cm	186 m 47 cm
− 9 m 92 cm	− 21 m 39 cm	− 29 m 86 cm

5.

21 m 84 cm	14 m 92 cm	139 m 34 cm
− 3 m 91 cm	− 8 m 97 cm	− 87 m 87 cm

The Millimetre (mm)

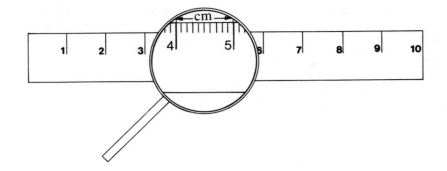

This line segment is 1 cm in length. ⌞____⌟
It is also 10 mm in length.
Therefore 1 cm is the same as 10 mm.

This line segment is 15 mm in length. ⌞____⌞⌟
Since 10 mm = 1 cm, it is also 1 cm 5 mm in length, or 1.5 cm.

A millimetre is a small length. Use calipers if necessary to measure the following lines.

Answers

1. ————————   _____ cm _____ mm

2. ————————————————————————————   _____ cm _____ mm

3. ————————————————————   _____ cm _____ mm

4. ——————————————   _____ cm _____ mm

5. ————   _____ cm _____ mm

6. ——————————————   _____ cm _____ mm

7. ————————————————————————   _____ cm _____ mm

8. ————————————————————————   _____ cm _____ mm

9. ——————————   _____ cm _____ mm

10. ————————   _____ cm _____ mm

Adding metric measurements:

1.
```
      9 mm
    + 7 mm
    ____ mm
= ____ cm ____ mm
```

```
      4 mm
    + 9 mm
    ____ mm
= ____cm ____ mm
```

```
      8 mm
      9 mm
    + 6 mm
    ____ mm
= ____ cm ____ mm
```

```
      6 mm
    + 8 mm
    ____ mm
= ____ cm ____ mm
```

```
      9 mm
      8 mm
    + 7 mm
    ____ mm
= ____ cm ____ mm
```

2.
```
  4 cm 6 mm
+ 8 cm 9 mm
```

```
  5 cm 9 mm
+ 9 cm 6 mm
```

```
  8 cm 9 mm
+ 3 cm 8 mm
```

3.
```
  13 cm 9 mm
  21 cm 3 mm
+ 36 cm 7 mm
```

```
  21 cm 8 mm
  36 cm 6 mm
+ 32 cm 7 mm
```

```
  36 cm 9 mm
  42 cm 3 mm
+  7 cm 7 mm
```

4.
```
  91 cm 9 mm
  36 cm 3 mm
  72 cm 6 mm
+ 45 cm 4 mm
```

```
  43 cm 9 mm
  61 cm 7 mm
  59 cm 8 mm
+ 26 cm 4 mm
```

```
  16 cm 8 mm
  82 cm 6 mm
  97 cm 7 mm
+ 36 cm 9 mm
```

5.
```
  1 m 36 cm 2 mm
  9 m 26 cm 4 mm
+ 3 m 93 cm 5 mm
```

```
  3 m 92 cm 8 mm
  9 m 16 cm 9 mm
+ 21 m 43 cm 6 mm
```

```
  92 m 21 cm 8 mm
  76 m 36 cm 3 mm
+ 43 m 59 cm 6 mm
```

Subtracting metric measurements:

1.   3 m 16 cm 9 mm   9 m 36 cm 7 mm   8 m 2 cm 9 mm
         − 2 m   4 cm 3 mm   − 7 m 21 cm 3 mm   − 3 m 1 cm 4 mm

2.   9 m 16 cm 3 mm   4 m 6 cm 1 mm   19 m 21 cm 3 mm
         − 2 m 12 cm 9 mm   − 2 m 3 cm 7 mm   − 10 m 13 cm 6 mm

3.   8 m 19 cm 6 mm   36 m 21 cm 9 mm   27 m 83 cm 2 mm
         − 3 m 12 cm 8 mm   −   18 cm 9 mm   −   9 mm

4.   13 m 8 cm 4 mm   26 m 8 cm 6 mm   47 m 81 cm 2 mm
         − 9 m 12 cm 6 mm   − 12 m 31 cm 9 mm   − 12 m 93 cm 6 mm

5.   43 m 21 cm 6 mm   93 m 4 cm 7 mm   86 m 9 cm 3 mm
         − 21 m 36 cm 9 mm   − 12 m 93 cm 9 mm   − 13 m 27 cm 9 mm

Multiplying metric measurements:

1.   36 cm   92 cm   13 mm   9 mm

               × 5   × 6   × 9   × 40

        = _____ cm   = _____ cm   = _____ mm   = _____ mm

         = ___ m ___ cm   = ___ m ___ cm   = ___ cm ___ mm   = ___ cm ___ mm

2.   3 cm 4 mm   93 cm 6 mm   39 cm 2 mm

              × 5   × 9   × 12

      _____ cm _____ mm   _____cm _____ mm   _____ cm _____ mm

      = ___ cm ___ mm   = ___ m ___ cm ___ mm   = ___ m ___ cm ___ mm

3.   2 m 13 cm 9 mm   13 m 47 cm 8 mm   83 m 23 cm 8 mm

              × 6   × 9   × 6

    _____ m _____ cm _____ mm   _____ m _____ cm _____ mm _____ m _____ cm _____ mm

  = ___ m ___ cm ___ mm = ___ m ___ cm ___ mm = ___ m ___ cm ___ mm

4.   440 m   326 m 64 cm   863 m   476 m

            × 9   × 8   × 10   × 6

          _____ m   _____ m _____ cm   _____ m   _____ m

  = ___ km ___ m = ___ km ___ m ___ cm = ___ km ___ m = ___ km ___ m

Conversions

Change:

176 mm = _____ cm _____ mm   187 cm = _____ m _____ cm

96 mm = _____ cm _____ mm   493 cm = _____ m _____ cm

196 mm = _____ cm _____ mm   126 cm = _____ m _____ cm

200 mm = _____ cm _____ mm   259 cm = _____ m _____ cm

27 mm = _____ cm _____ mm   324 cm = _____ m _____ cm

2 cm = _____ mm   1 m = _____ cm

9 cm = _____ mm   6 m = _____ cm

18 cm = _____ mm   3 m = _____ cm

23 cm = _____ mm   12 m = _____ cm

47 cm = _____ mm   2 m = _____ cm

Change to lowest terms:

3 m 126 cm 19 mm = _____ m _____ cm _____ mm

2 m 326 cm 47 mm = _____ m _____ cm _____ mm

9 m   96 cm 13 mm = _____ m _____ cm _____ mm

7 m 127 cm 21 mm = _____ m _____ cm _____ mm

3 m 346 cm 16 mm = _____ m _____ cm _____ mm

4 m 873 cm 87 mm = _____ m _____ cm _____ mm

12 m 267 cm 48 mm = _____ m _____ cm _____ mm

8 m 543 cm 93 mm = _____ m _____ cm _____ mm

6 m 647 cm 76 mm = _____ m _____ cm _____ mm

12 m 396 cm 59 mm = _____ m _____ cm _____ mm

Measuring Myself

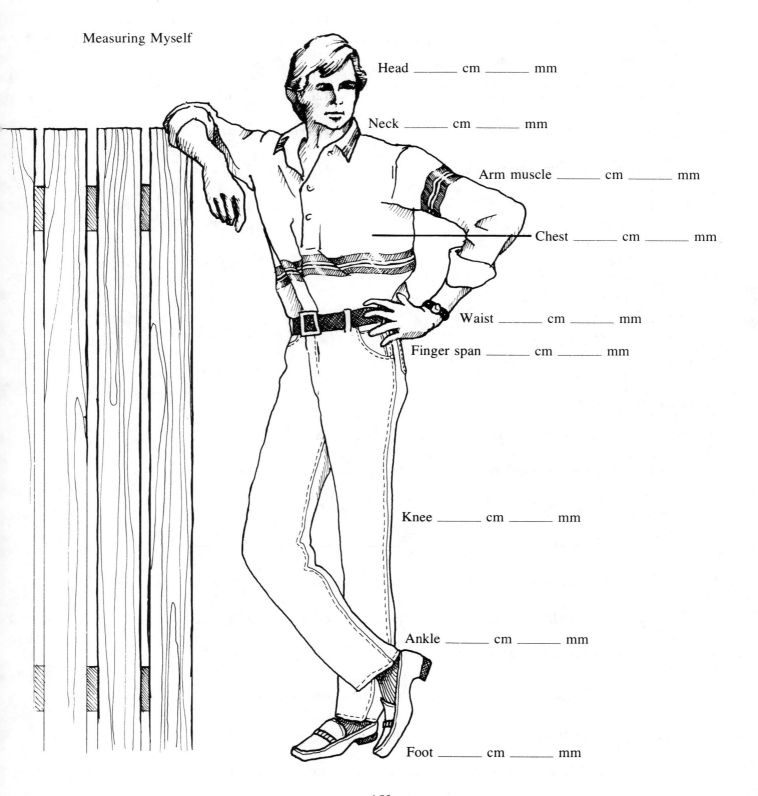

Head _____ cm _____ mm

Neck _____ cm _____ mm

Arm muscle _____ cm _____ mm

Chest _____ cm _____ mm

Waist _____ cm _____ mm

Finger span _____ cm _____ mm

Knee _____ cm _____ mm

Ankle _____ cm _____ mm

Foot _____ cm _____ mm

Situation Solving

1. The largest fish Susie caught measured about 60 cm. How many mm was that?

2. The winner of a high jump leaped 1 m 86 cm. Express the height of his jump in m.

3. The diameter of a quarter is 24 mm. The diameter of a dime is 18 mm. What is the difference in diameters?

4. Ann is 1.2 m and Betty is 133 cm. Who is taller and by how much?

5. Zarack was 43 cm long when born. His brother Kai was 57 cm long when born. How much longer was Kai?

6. Find the average length of five pieces of candy whose lengths are 28 mm, 41 mm, 35 mm, 39 mm and 38 mm. Express your answer in cm.

7. Biagio jogs 3 km per day, 5 days per week, 50 weeks per year. How many km does he jog per year?

8. If Charisse is 1.67 m tall, how many cm tall is she?

9. The Smiths drove their car an average of 15 000 km per year. How far did they drive in five years?

10. How far would a car travel in 6 h at an average speed of 80 km/h?

Calculating Perimeter

Meaning of perimeter:

Jim Bradshaw has decided to protect his shrubs and flowers by putting a fence around his property. Before he orders the fencing he must know how many metres of it he requires.

Study the diagram of Jim's property and answer the questions.

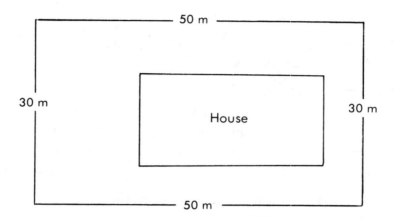

1. What is the length of the lot? _____

2. What is the width of the lot?_____

3. What is the distance around the lot?_____

4. How many metres of fencing does he need? _____

5. What parts of the lot have the same dimensions?   (a)_____

    (b)_____

6. What numbers did you add to find the distance around the lot? (a)_____(b)_____(c)_____(d)_____

The distance around a rectangle or square is called the <u>perimeter</u>.

There are two ways of finding the perimeter of Jim's lot.

Method 1: Add the length + width + length + width.

$$50 + 30 + 50 + 30 = 160$$

Method 2: Use a formula.

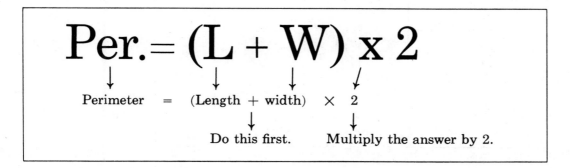

This is how Jim used the formula to find the perimeter of his lot.

$$
\begin{aligned}
\text{Per.} \;=\; &(L + W) & \times\; 2 \\
=\; &(50 + 30) & \times\; 2 \\
=\; &\quad 80 & \times\; 2 \\
\\
=\; &\quad 160 &
\end{aligned}
$$

The distance around the lot is 160 m. Jim will need to order 160 m of fencing.

Use the formula to find the perimeter of each lot:

1. The Smiths' lot: 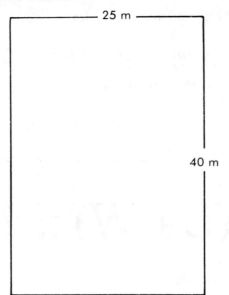 Work here:

2. The Browns' lot: Work here:

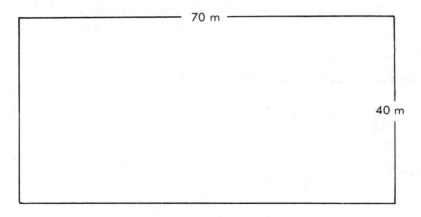

3. The Whites' lot: 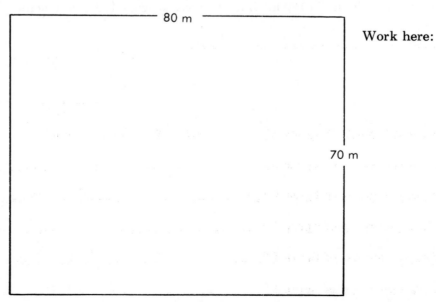 Work here:

Find the perimeter of the following rectangles. Use the formula.

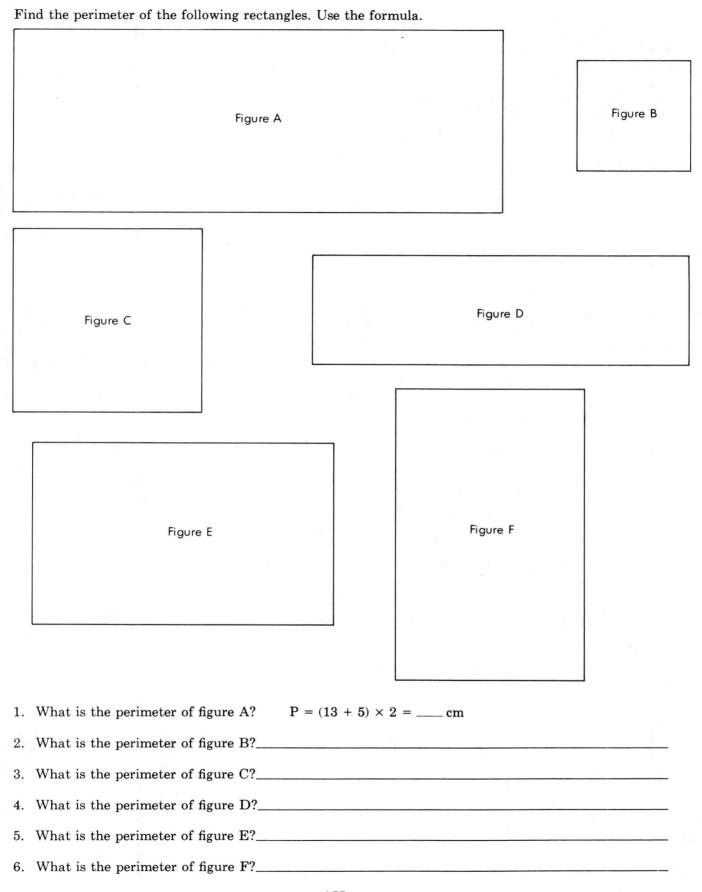

Figure A

Figure B

Figure C

Figure D

Figure E

Figure F

1. What is the perimeter of figure A?   P = (13 + 5) × 2 = ＿＿ cm

2. What is the perimeter of figure B?＿＿＿＿＿＿＿＿＿＿＿＿＿＿＿＿＿＿＿＿＿

3. What is the perimeter of figure C?＿＿＿＿＿＿＿＿＿＿＿＿＿＿＿＿＿＿＿＿＿

4. What is the perimeter of figure D?＿＿＿＿＿＿＿＿＿＿＿＿＿＿＿＿＿＿＿＿＿

5. What is the perimeter of figure E?＿＿＿＿＿＿＿＿＿＿＿＿＿＿＿＿＿＿＿＿＿

6. What is the perimeter of figure F?＿＿＿＿＿＿＿＿＿＿＿＿＿＿＿＿＿＿＿＿＿

Find the perimeter:

	Dimensions		(l + w)	Work Here	X 2	Answer
	length	width				
1.	5 cm	3 cm	(5 + 3)	$\begin{array}{r} 5 \\ + 3 \\ \hline 8 \end{array}$ 8 × 2 = 16	16	16 cm
2.	6 m	4 m				
3.	30 m	46 m				
4.	5 cm	6 cm				
5.	3 m	9 m				
6.	26 m	47 m				
7.	29 mm	83 mm				
8.	62 m	83 m				
9.	47 m	86 m				

156

Find the perimeter:

	Dimensions		(l + w)	Work Here	X 2	Answer
	length	width				
1.	7 m	4 m				
2.	9 km	4 km				
3.	23 cm	16 cm				
4.	40 m	26 m				
5.	17 m	23 m				
6.	29 mm	36 mm				
7.	21 cm	73 cm				
8.	29 m	47 m				
9.	86 cm	23 cm				

Find the perimeter. Be sure to convert your answer to the largest units where necessary. (Use only the common units m, cm, mm.)

	Dimensions		(l + w)	Work Here	X 2	Converted Answer
	length	width				
1.	120 cm	90 cm	(120 + 90)	120 + 90 210 × 2 420	420 cm	4 m 20 cm
2.	10 m	4 m				
3.	16 m	18 m				
4.	43 cm	141 cm				
5.	86 cm	42 cm				
6.	74 cm	26 cm				
7.	76 m	48 m				
8.	36 cm	18 cm				
9.	24 mm	18 mm				

The formula can be used only when you are finding the perimeter of a rectangle or square. When you are finding the perimeter of an odd-shaped object you must measure and add the length of all the sides.

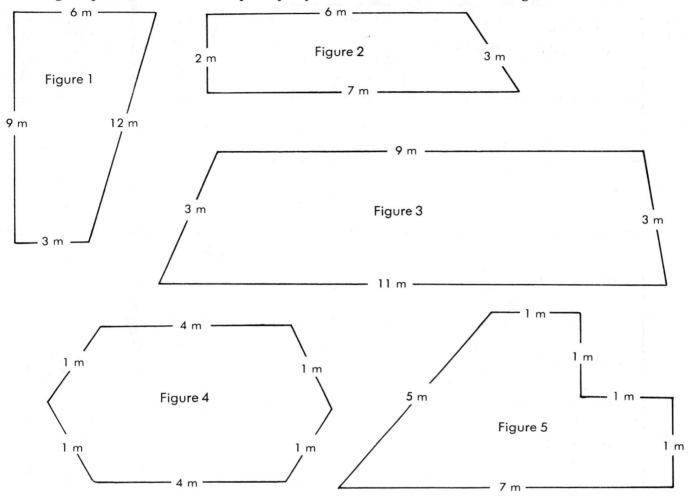

Find the perimeter of:

Figure	Work Here	Converted Answer
1		
2		
3		
4		
5		

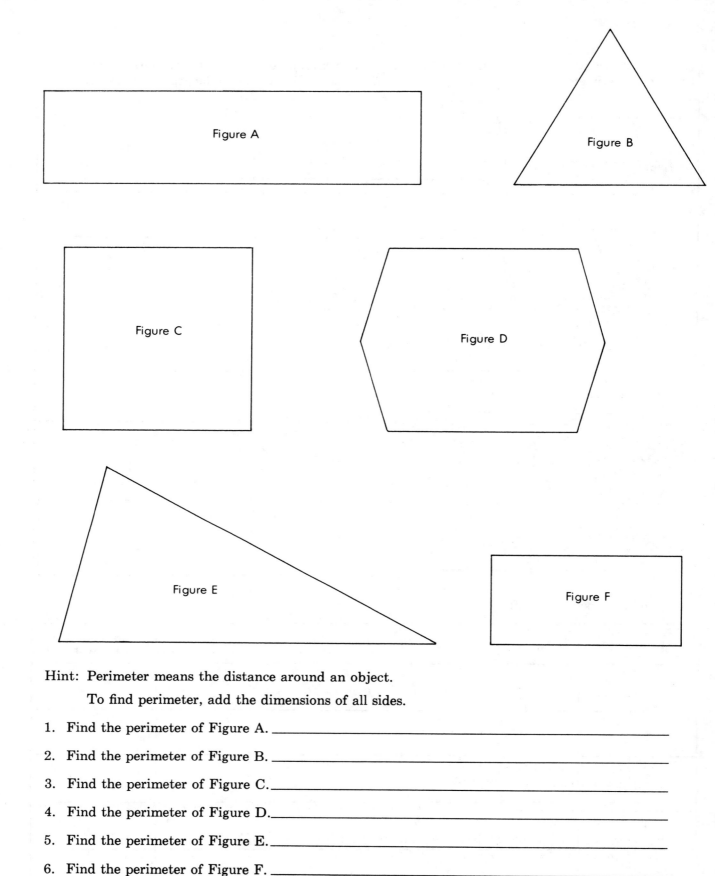

Figure A

Figure B

Figure C

Figure D

Figure E

Figure F

Hint: Perimeter means the distance around an object.

To find perimeter, add the dimensions of all sides.

1. Find the perimeter of Figure A. _____

2. Find the perimeter of Figure B. _____

3. Find the perimeter of Figure C. _____

4. Find the perimeter of Figure D. _____

5. Find the perimeter of Figure E. _____

6. Find the perimeter of Figure F. _____

Situation Solving

1. Find the perimeter of a chessboard 32 cm on each side.

2. The perimeter of a square table is 680 mm. What is the length of each side?

3. How much would it cost to fence a yard 32 m by 25 m if fencing cost $1.30 per metre?

4. Find the perimeter of a rectangle 28 cm long and 18 cm wide.

5. Find the cost of weatherstripping for a window 87 cm long and 158 cm wide at a cost of 50¢/m.

6. A room is 3.4 m by 4.6 m. How much baseboard is required to go around the room?

7. If Paul jogged around the block 3 times, and the block was 67 m by 83 m, how far did he run?

8. Ceiling molding cost 85¢ per m. How much would it cost for a room 4.6 m by 3.4 m?

9. How much framing material would be required to make 5 large frames each measuring 4.7 m by 3.3 m?

10. Joe is making 4 coffee tables. Each one measures 1.4 m by 0.6 m. If wood trim costs 50¢/m, how much will it cost to trim all four tables?

Calculating Area

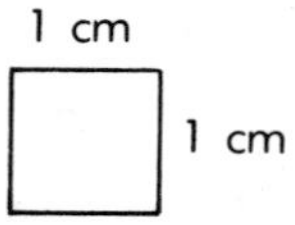

1. What is the length of the above diagram?____________________

2. What is its width?____________________

3. What name is given to the shape of the above diagram?____________________

Since the diagram is a square, and is 1 cm long and 1 cm wide, it is called ONE SQUARE CENTIMETRE or 1 cm^2.

Area of a Rectangle

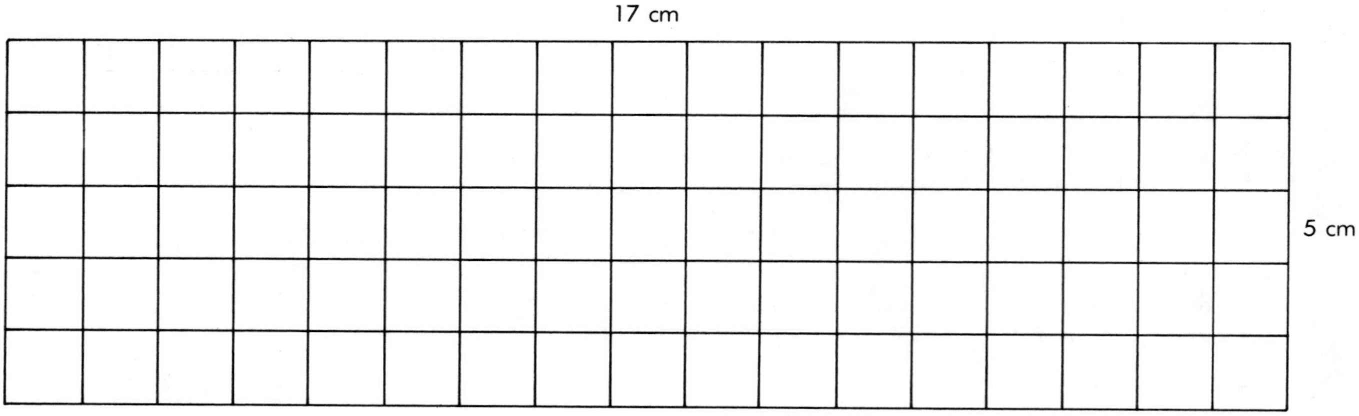

1. What is the length of the above diagram?____________________

2. What is its width? ____________________

3. Count the number of 1-cm squares. ____________________

4. What is the area of the above rectangle? ____________________

> Hint: Area means THE AMOUNT OF SURFACE AN OBJECT COVERS.

5. Rather than counting the square centimetres, what other method could be used to find the area?

____

____

This is the formula for finding the area of a rectangle.

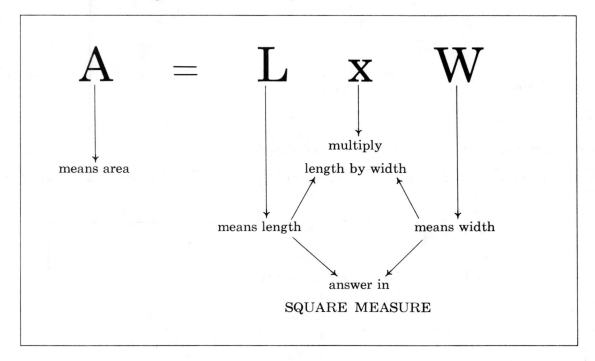

1. What is the length of the rectangle?_____

2. What is the width of the rectangle?_____

3. This is how area is found:

   Area = l × w

   Area = _____ × _____ = _____ cm²

   Remember:
   Write square
   centimetres
   as cm².

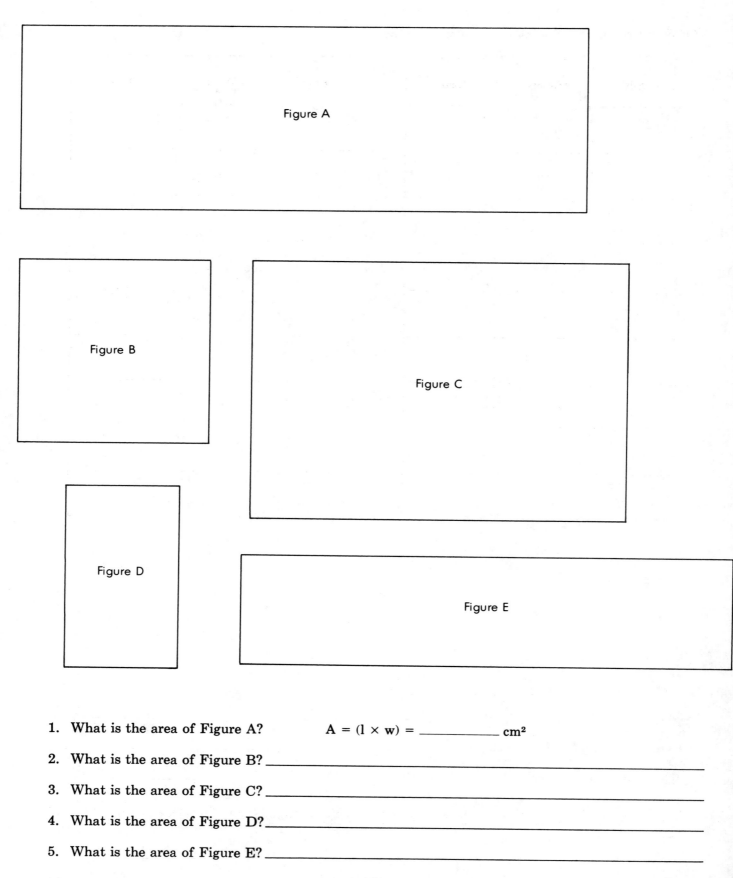

Figure A

Figure B

Figure C

Figure D

Figure E

1. What is the area of Figure A?   A = (l × w) = _____ cm²

2. What is the area of Figure B? _____

3. What is the area of Figure C? _____

4. What is the area of Figure D? _____

5. What is the area of Figure E? _____

Complete the charts:

Length	Width	Area
4 cm	6 cm	
9 cm	8 cm	
12 m	6 m	
18 m	3 m	
6 km	3 km	
14 cm	20 cm	
46 m	21 m	
18 mm	36 mm	
96 cm	4 cm	

Length	Width	Area
36 cm	24 cm	
76 km	21 km	
108 cm	97 cm	
36 m	9 m	
17 m	48 m	
108 mm	7 mm	
144 cm	6 cm	
9 cm	36 cm	
72 m	4 m	

Area of a Triangle

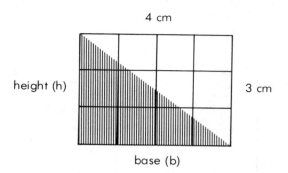

height (h)   4 cm   3 cm

base (b)

The area of the above rectangle is $(4 \times 3) = 12$ cm². It is easy to see that the area of the shaded part of the rectangle, which forms a triangle, is ½ of 12 cm², or 6 cm².

Of course, not all triangles will fit so neatly into a rectangle. However, they can always be made to fit into *two* rectangles. Study the triangle below.

As it is, there is no way to fit it into a rectangle, but if you draw a line from one corner to meet the opposite side at *right angles*, it is changed into two triangles that will fit into rectangles.

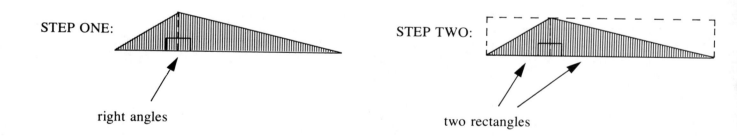

STEP ONE: STEP TWO:

right angles   two rectangles

Now it is an easy matter to calculate the areas of the two triangles and add them up.

If you work it out, you will see that the area of any triangle is equal to one half of its *base* (any side) times its *height* (the distance straight up from that side to the opposite corner).

From this we can see that the area of a triangle is given by the formula

$$A = \frac{1}{2} (b \times h)$$

where *b* is the base of the triangle and *h* is the height.

Example:

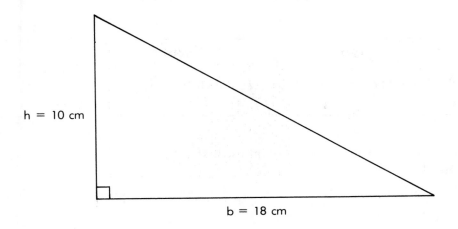

h = 10 cm

b = 18 cm

The area of the above triangle is, by the formula, $\frac{1}{2}$ (10 × 18) = $\frac{1}{2}$ × 180 = 90 cm².

Find the areas of these triangles by measuring and calculating:

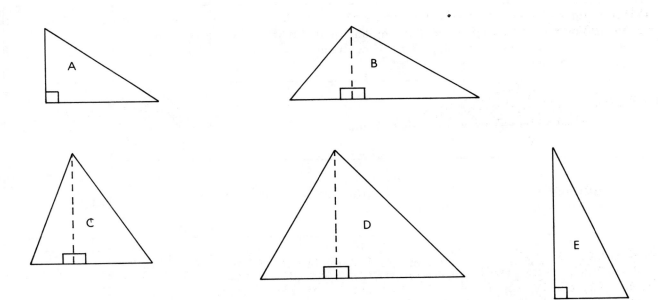

A

B

C

D

E

Answers: A _____ B _____ C _____ D _____ E _____

Situation Solving

1. Chris mowed a lawn 22 m by 17 m. What area did Chris mow?

2. What is the area in square metres of a counter top with a length of 3.4 m and a width of 0.6 m?

3. How much carpet is required for a room 5.6 m by 6.2 m?

4. How much would it cost to replace a window 240 cm by 360 cm if glass costs $3.00/m?

5. How much would it cost to sod a playing field 110 m by 55 m at a cost of 65¢/m²?

6. A conservation area measured 6.3 km long and 4.8 km wide. Spraying mosquitoes costs $30.00/km². How much does it cost to spray the conservation area?

7. Find the area of a square whose side is 7 mm.

8. A farmer averages 7 bales of hay per dam². How many bales of hay would he bale from a field 150 m by 320 m?

9. A fireplace measures 3 m by 2 m. How many bricks will be required if a brick measures 100 cm²? (Hint: Change fireplace measurements to cm.)

10. The students in Textiles were making skirts. How many skirts can be made from 28 m² of material if each skirt requires 1.4 m² of material?

Volume—Dry or Cubic Measurement

This is the formula for finding "dry" volume.

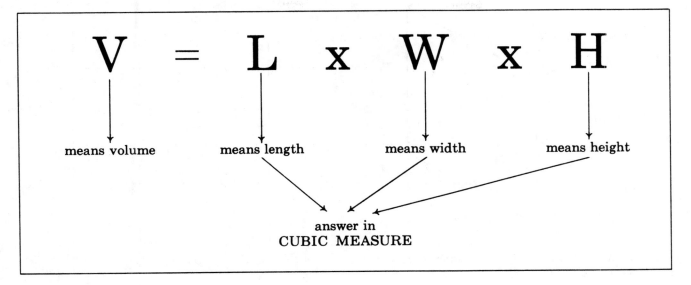

$$V \quad = \quad L \quad x \quad W \quad x \quad H$$

means volume means length means width means height

answer in
CUBIC MEASURE

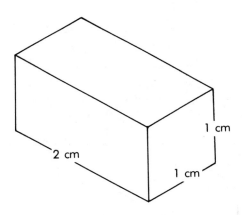

1 cm

2 cm

1 cm

1. What is the length?_____

(Note: The diagram, like others in this book, is drawn to scale and is not actual size.)

2. What is the width?_____

3. What is the height?_____

4. What is the volume?

$V = l \times w \times h$

$V = 2 \times 1 \times 1 =$ _____ cubic centimetres or _____ cm³

> Remember:
> Write cubic centimetres
> as cm³.

169

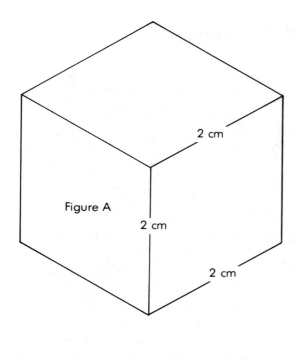

2 cm

Figure A

2 cm

2 cm

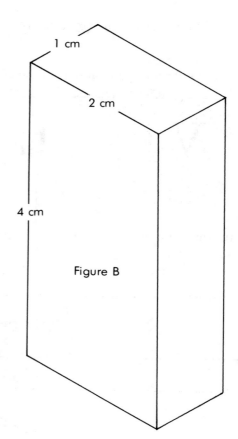

1 cm

2 cm

4 cm

Figure B

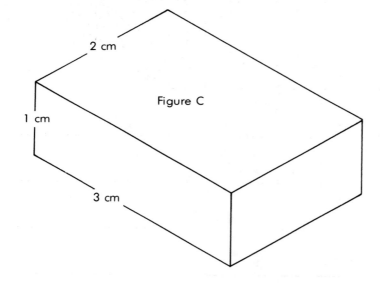

2 cm

Figure C

1 cm

3 cm

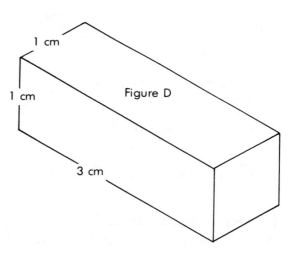

1 cm

1 cm

Figure D

3 cm

1. What is the volume of Figure A? _____

2. What is the volume of Figure B? _____

3. What is the volume of Figure C? _____

4. What is the volume of Figure D? _____

This is the figure of a box divided into 1-cm cubes (enlarged).

1. What is the volume of Section A?_____

2. What is the volume of Section B?_____

3. What is the volume of Section C?_____

4. What is the volume of the box?_____

5. How many times can Section A be fitted into the box?_____

6. How many times can Section B be fitted into the box?_____

7. How much space would remain in the box if Section C was removed?_____

_____

Find the volume for the dimensions given below:

Length	Width	Height	Work Here	Volume
4 cm	7 cm	4 cm		
6 mm	8 mm	16 mm		
8 m	10 m	3 m		
2 km	14 km	8 km		
1 m	15 m	7 m		
23 cm	6 cm	2 cm		
4 cm	23 cm	6 cm		
19 mm	4 mm	3 mm		
7 cm	9 cm	14 cm		
6 m	8 m	3 m		
15 km	7 km	7 km		
8 cm	6 cm	10 cm		
9 m	2 m	16 m		
4 m	5 m	19 m		
3 mm	3 mm	4 mm		
7 mm	9 mm	12 mm		
6 cm	14 cm	20 cm		

Volume—Fluid or Capacity Measurement

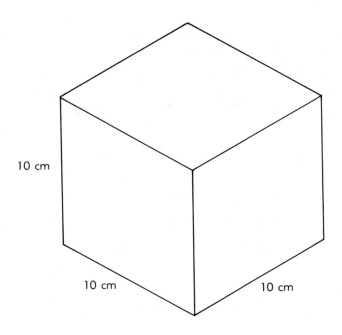

10 cm

10 cm   10 cm

The volume of the above cube is 10 cm × 10 cm × 10 cm = 1000 cm³. However, this volume can also be expressed in *fluid* or *capacity* units (units which do not involve measurements of length, and which are used mainly for describing how much fluid a container holds).

Thus, the volume of the cube above is also one *litre*. The litre is the basic metric unit of fluid measurement.

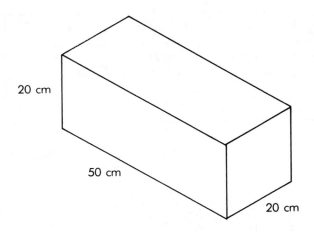

20 cm

50 cm   20 cm

The volume of the box above is 20 cm × 50 cm × 20 cm = 20 000 cm³ (dry units), *or* 20 litres (fluid units).

Find the dry volume and the capacity of these containers.

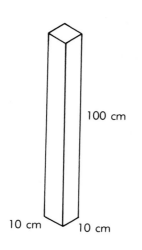

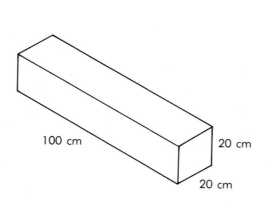

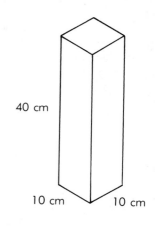

dry volume   _____ cm³   dry volume   _____ cm³   dry volume   _____ cm³

capacity   _____ litres   capacity   _____ litres   capacity   _____ litres

The most commonly used units of fluid volume or capacity are:

kilolitre	kL	centilitre	cL
litre	L	millilitre	mL

The prefixes for fluid volume or capacity, and their symbols, are the same as those for length. Only the basic unit is different.

kilo-	hecto-	deca-	(litre)	deci-	centi-	milli-
k	h	da	(L)	d	c	m
1000 ×	100 ×	10 ×	—	$\times \dfrac{1}{10}$	$\times \dfrac{1}{100}$	$\times \dfrac{1}{1000}$

Change to L:

1. 1000 mL _____ L
2. 500 mL _____ L
3. 2000 mL _____ L
4. 100 mL _____ L
5. 1 mL _____ L

Change to mL:

1. 2.5 L _____ mL
2. 4.3 L _____ mL
3. 0.75 L _____ mL
4. 0.50 L _____ mL
5. 0.01 L _____ mL

Mass and Weight

Mass is the measure of the amount of material in an object. *Weight* is the measure of the force of gravity on an object. On earth the mass of an object and its weight are almost equal, so we can interchange the two.

In the metric system the basic unit of mass is the *gram*.

The most common units for the measurement of mass are the following:

kilogram	kg
gram	g
milligram	mg

Again, the prefixes are the same as those in length and in fluid volume, and so are the symbols except for the basic unit.

kilo-	hecto-	deca-	(*gram*)	deci-	centi-	milli-
k	h	da	(g)	d	c	m
1000 ×	100 ×	10 ×	—	$\times \dfrac{1}{10}$	$\times \dfrac{1}{100}$	$\times \dfrac{1}{1000}$

Fill in the blanks:

1. 1 g = _____ mg

2. 1 kg = _____ g

3. 10 kg = _____ mg

4. 10 kg = _____ g

5. 1000 mg = _____ g

6. 2500 g = _____ kg

7. 8.6 g = _____ mg

8. 12.5 kg = _____ g

9. 285 mg = _____ g

10. 0.05 kg = _____ g

Estimate the mass of the following. With the aid of a metric scale check your estimate for accuracy.

	Estimated	Actual
1. Me	_____	_____
2. My math teacher	_____	_____
3. My principal	_____	_____
4. A guest at the school	_____	_____
5. Classmate 1	_____	_____
6. Classmate 2	_____	_____
7. Classmate 3	_____	_____
8. Classmate 4	_____	_____
9. Classmate 5	_____	_____
10. Classmate 6	_____	_____
11. This math book	_____	_____
12. A litre of water	_____	_____
13. 1 concrete block	_____	_____
14. 1 brick	_____	_____
15. 4 L of paint	_____	_____
16. A pair of shoes	_____	_____
17. A radio	_____	_____
18. A TV set	_____	_____

Temperature

Temperature is measured in degrees Celsius (centigrade).

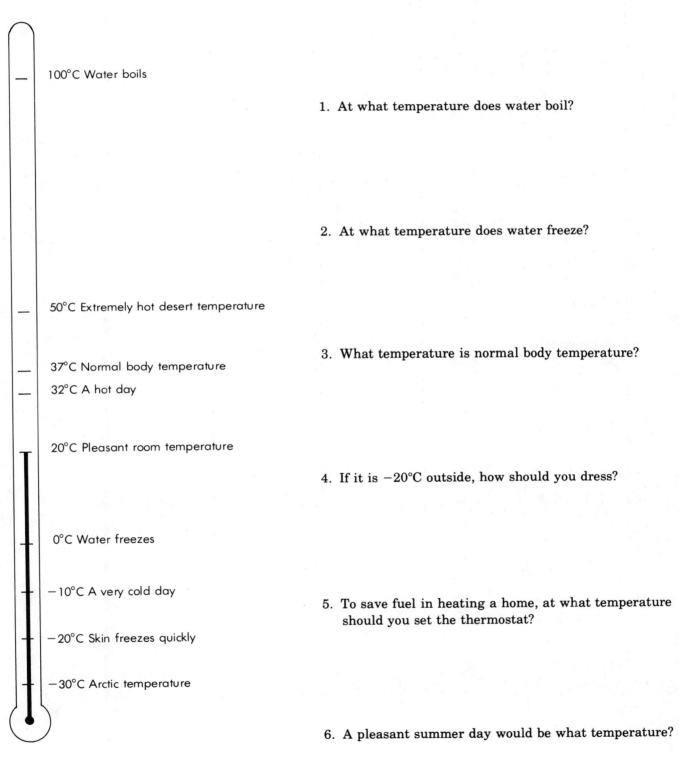

1. At what temperature does water boil?

2. At what temperature does water freeze?

3. What temperature is normal body temperature?

4. If it is −20°C outside, how should you dress?

5. To save fuel in heating a home, at what temperature should you set the thermostat?

6. A pleasant summer day would be what temperature?

Test Your Skill

1. Measure these lines.

(a) _____   _____

(b) _____   _____

(c) _____   _____

(d) ____   _____

(e) _____   _____

2. Add:

$$\begin{array}{r} 9 \text{ m } 4 \text{ cm} \\ + 3 \text{ m } 7 \text{ cm} \\ \hline \end{array} \qquad \begin{array}{r} 26 \text{ cm} \\ + 34 \text{ cm} \\ \hline \end{array} \qquad \begin{array}{r} 3 \text{ m } 6 \text{ cm } 9 \text{ mm} \\ + 4 \text{ m } 21 \text{ cm } 8 \text{ mm} \\ \hline \end{array}$$

3. Subtract:

$$\begin{array}{r} 29 \text{ cm} \\ - 14 \text{ cm} \\ \hline \end{array} \qquad \begin{array}{r} 1 \text{ m } 13 \text{ cm } 13 \text{ mm} \\ - 47 \text{ cm } 3 \text{ mm} \\ \hline \end{array} \qquad \begin{array}{r} 14 \text{ m } 6 \text{ cm } 2 \text{ mm} \\ - 3 \text{ m } 87 \text{ cm } 9 \text{ mm} \\ \hline \end{array}$$

4. Fill in the blanks:

(a) 9742 m _____ km

(b) 4893 m _____ km

(c) 476 cm _____ m

(d) 974 cm _____ m

(e) 1000 mm _____ cm

5. Find the perimeter of the following rectangles. Convert your answer to largest units.

(a) length 18 m, width 27 m

(b) length 23 cm, width 18 m

(c) length 97 m, width 43 m

(d) length 47 cm, width 36 m

(e) length 17 cm, width 24 cm

6. Find the area of the following rectangles and convert to largest units.
(a) 23 m by 18 m
(b) 76 cm by 42 cm
(c) 34 m by 18 m
(d) 76 mm by 14 mm
(e) 23 m by 46 m

7. Find the area of the following triangles and convert to largest units.
(a) height 10 cm   base   8 cm
(b) height   3 m   base   4 m
(c) height   9 m   base 18 m
(d) height 14 cm   base 32 cm
(e) height 23 m   base 46 m

8. Find the volume of the following rectangular shapes.
(a) length   3 cm   width   5 cm   height   8 cm
(b) length   9 m   width   4 m   height   6 m
(c) length   4 cm   width   9 cm   height   7 cm
(d) length 14 mm   width 12 mm   height   6 mm
(e) length   9 m   width 14 m   height 12 m

9. Change to L:
(a) 2000 mL _____ L
(b)   50 mL _____ L
(c) 3500 mL _____ L
(d)   1 mL _____ L
(e)   150 mL _____ L

10. Change to mL:
(a)   25 L = _____ mL
(b) 0.5   L = _____ mL
(c)   4 L = _____ mL
(d) 0.75 L = _____ mL
(e) 2.6 L = _____ mL

11. Fill in the blanks:
(a) 1 g = _____ mg
(b) 1 kg = _____ g
(c) 2000 kg = _____ g
(d) 1500 kg = _____ g
(e) 25 g = _____ mg

12. At what temperature does water freeze? _____

13. At what temperature does water boil? _____

14. At what temperature is it comfortable without a coat? _____

CHAPTER SIX
PART-TIME JOBS

Lawn Maintenance

John felt that since he would soon be 16, he would like to own a car. After discussion with his parents it was decided that if he could earn the money to buy, insure and operate the car, he could buy it on his sixteenth birthday.

John planned to earn money by cutting lawns. He charged $2.50 per lawn, and used his own equipment to do the job.

Earnings for one week:

Monday   23 — Mr. Smith's lawn

Tuesday   24 — Mr. Clark's lawn

Wednesday 25 — Mr. Reed's lawn

Thursday   26 — Mrs. Jones' lawn

Friday   27 — Mr. East's lawn

Saturday   28 — Mr. Green's lawn

                    — Mr. Bonde's lawn

Fill in the chart below to show John's earnings for one week.

Day	Date	Name of Employer	Earnings	
		Total		

What are John's earnings for the week?_____

John increased his earnings by trimming and spraying as well as mowing. He had extra expenses for trimming and spraying, so he set his rates as:

Mow — $5.00
Trim — $2.00
Spray — $2.75 per hour

This is a list of John's earnings and expenses:

Monday	5 —	Mow and trim
Tuesday	6 —	Mow
	6 —	Spray (2 hours)
Wednesday	7 —	Bought shears for $5.50
	7 —	Bought gloves for $1.79
	7 —	Mow and trim
Thursday	8 —	Bought spray for $3.50
	8 —	Spray (2 hours)
Friday	9 —	Mow
	9 —	Mow and trim
Saturday	10 —	Mow
	10 —	Mow and spray (4 hours)
	10 —	Attended show $3.00

Complete the chart to find John's savings.

Day	Date	Job	Total		Day	Date	Expenses	Total	
		Total					Total		

Total Income		
Total Expenses		
Savings		

Calculating Hours Worked

When working at a part-time job, it is wise to find the total number of hours worked and to calculate the wages earned so you can check to make sure that the employer has made no error in calculating your wage. To check your wage you must know the number of hours worked.

1. How many hours are there from:

   (a) 9:00 a.m. to 10:00 a.m. _____

   (b) 10:00 a.m. to 11:00 a.m. _____

   (c) 11:00 a.m. to 12:00 noon _____

   (d) 9:00 a.m. to 12:00 noon _____

   (e) 12:00 noon to 1:00 p.m. _____

   (f) 1:00 p.m. to 2:00 p.m. _____

   (g) 2:00 p.m. to 3:00 p.m. _____

   (h) 12:00 noon to 3:00 p.m. _____

   (i) 9:00 a.m. to 3:00 p.m. _____

2. Complete the chart below.

Start	Quit	Hours	Start	Quit	Total
8:00	12:00		8:00	3:00	
9:00	12:00		9:00	5:00	
7:00	12:00		10:00	4:00	
10:00	12:00		8:00	5:00	
12:00	5:00		11.00	6:00	
12:00	3:00		8:00	4:00	
12:00	2:00		11:00	3:00	
12:00	4:00		10:00	5:00	
11:00	1:00		9:00	6:00	
10:00	2:00		11:00	5:00	
9:00	4:00		9:00	2:00	
10:00	3:00		9:00	3:00	
11:00	4:00		11:00	2:00	

3. Fill in the hours:

In	Out	Hours	In	Out	Hours
8:00	10:00		9:00	11:00	
9:00	10:00		8:00	12:00	
8:00	12:00		10:00	12:00	
10:00	12:00		11:00	1:00	
10:00	1:00		8:00	1:00	
11:00	1:00		11:00	5:00	
9:00	1:00		12:00	2:00	
9:00	5:00		8:00	5:00	
10:00	2:00		10:00	6:00	
11:00	3:00		1:00	9:00	
2:00	3:00		2:00	9:00	
1:00	6:00		11:00	7:00	
9:00	2:00		8:00	7:00	
10:00	5:00		11:00	6:00	
8:00	3:00		1:00	8:00	
10:00	8:00		12:00	9:00	
2:00	7:00		8:00	6:00	
10:00	7:00		9:00	7:00	
2:00	3:00		11:00	4:00	
9:00	4:00		1:00	7:00	
12:00	8:00		10:00	4:00	
12:00	7:00		12:00	5:00	
2:00	4:00		9:00	12:00	
12:00	6:00		2:00	8:00	

4. Complete the time card below. All wages are for $3.00 an hour.

In	Out	Hours	Wages
8:00	2:00		
9:00	4:00		
8:00	3:00		
8:00	5:00		
9:00	6:00		
12:00	3:00		
1:00	6:00		
4:00	6:00		
11:00	4:00		
10:00	5:00		
9:00	3:00		
9:00	5:00		
10:00	2:00		
11:00	3:00		

5. How many hours are there from:

   (a) 11:30 a.m. to 12:30 p.m. _____

   (b) 10:30 a.m. to 12:30 p.m. _____

   (c) 12:30 p.m. to 1:30 p.m. _____

   (d) 12:30 p.m. to 2:30 p.m. _____

   (e) 10:30 a.m. to 2:30 p.m. _____

6. Complete the chart to find the number of hours worked.

Start	Quit	Hours	Start	Quit	Hours
12:30	4:30		10:30	6:30	
8:30	2:30		7:30	3:30	
9:30	3:30		11:30	4:30	
7:30	1:30		9:30	5:30	
10:30	5:30		12:30	7:30	
11:30	6:30		8:30	5:30	
8.30	4:30		9:30	4:30	

Overtime

Most babysitters charge a regular rate before midnight and an overtime rate after midnight. They must find the regular hours worked to midnight and the overtime hours worked after midnight before they can calculate their total earnings.

Monday   — 8:00 p.m. to 2:00 a.m.
Tuesday   — 7:00 p.m. to 3:00 a.m.
Wednesday — 9:00 p.m. to 2:00 a.m.

Day	Regular (to midnight)			Overtime (after midnight)			Total Hours
	Start	Quit	Hours	Start	Quit	Hours	
Mon.	8:00	12:00	4	12:00	2:00	2	4 regular 2 overtime
Tues.	7:00	12:00	5	12:00	3:00	3	
Wed.	9:00	2:00	5			7	

Babysitter

In order to make spending money, Mary decided to take babysitting jobs. She charged a regular rate of $2.00 an hour to midnight and an overtime rate of $2.50 after midnight.

Mary's working hours for the first week were:

Monday	— 5:30 p.m. — 7:30 p.m.
Tuesday	— 6:00 p.m. — 9:00 p.m.
Wednesday	— 6:30 p.m. — 10:30 p.m.
Thursday	— 5:00 p.m. — 11:00 p.m.
Friday	— 7:00 p.m. — 1:00 a.m.
Saturday	— 2:30 p.m. — 5:30 p.m.
	— 7:00 p.m. — 2:00 a.m.

Day	Regular (to midnight)			Overtime (after midnight)			Total
	Start	Quit	Total	Start at 12:00	Quit	Total	
					Total		

What were Mary's total earnings for the first week? _____

Mary's working hours for the second week were:

Monday — 5:00 p.m. — 9:00 p.m.
Tuesday — 7:00 p.m. — 10:00 p.m.
Wednesday — 4:30 p.m. — 10:30 p.m.
Thursday — 6:00 p.m. — 10:30 p.m.
Friday — 7:00 p.m. — 1:00 a.m.
Saturday — 1:30 p.m. — 4:30 p.m.
— 6:00 p.m. — 3:00 a.m.

| Day | Regular (to midnight) | | | Overtime (after midnight) | | | Total |
	Start	Quit	Total	Start at 12:00	Quit	Total	
					Total		

What were Mary's total earnings for the second week? _____

Mary's working hours for the third week were:

Monday	—	5:00 p.m.	—	1:00 a.m.
Tuesday	—	6:00 p.m.	—	9:00 p.m.
Wednesday	—	7:00 p.m.	—	3:00 a.m.
Thursday	—	6:00 p.m.	—	9:00 p.m.
Friday	—	5:30 p.m.	—	11:30 p.m.
Saturday	—	2:30 p.m.	—	5:30 p.m.
	—	6:00 p.m.	—	2:00 a.m.

Day	Regular (to midnight)			Overtime (after midnight)			Total
	Start	Quit	Total	Start at 12:00	Quit	Total	
					Total		

What were Mary's total earnings for the third week? _____

Mary's working hours for the fourth week were:

Monday	— 5:00 p.m. —	1:00 a.m.
Tuesday	— 5:30 p.m. —	9:30 p.m.
Wednesday	— 7:00 p.m. —	2:00 a.m.
Thursday	— 6:00 p.m. —	9:00 p.m.
Friday	— 7:00 p.m. —	3:00 a.m.
Saturday	— 2:30 p.m. —	5:30 p.m.
	— 7:30 p.m. —	10:30 p.m.

	Regular (to midnight)			Overtime (after midnight)				
Day	Start	Quit	Total	Start at 12:00	Quit	Total		Total
						Total		

What were Mary's total earnings for the fourth week? _____

Complete the following chart to find Mary's total earnings for the four weeks.

First Week Total		
Second Week Total		
Third Week Total		
Fourth Week Total		
Total Income		

On the chart below, list Mary's earnings under Income and the money she spent under Expenses.

Expenses:
1. Student Activity Card . . . . $ 1.50
2. Clothing 9.00
3. Cosmetics 2.75
4. Gift 8.39
5. Swimming Class 2.00
6. School Supplies 4.50
7. Entertainment 6.00
8. Ring 14.59

Week	Income	Total	Item	Expenses	Total
1			1		
2			2		
3			3		
4			4		
			5		
			6		
			7		
			8		
Total				Total	

Mary's total income _____

Mary's total expenses _____

Mary's total profit _____

Cashier

During the summer Sandy got a part-time job working at the corner grocery store. Sandy earned $3.80 an hour. Sandy worked the following hours:

First Week: Monday   —8 h   Third Week: Monday   —4 h
                    Tuesday   —5 h   Wednesday—6 h
                    Wednesday —5 h   Thursday   —4 h
                    Thursday —5 h   Saturday —8 h
                    Friday   —8 h
                    Saturday —8 h

Second Week: Monday   —4 h   Fourth Week: Tuesday   —4 h
                    Tuesday   —6 h   Wednesday—5 h
                    Friday   —6 h   Friday   —6 h
                    Saturday —8 h   Saturday —8 h

Use the following chart to help determine Sandy's time and wages for the month.

Day	First Week	Second Week	Third Week	Fourth Week
Monday				
Tuesday				
Wednesday				
Thursday				
Friday				
Saturday				
Total Hours				
Earned Wages				

Complete the following chart to find Sandy's total earnings for the four weeks.

First Week Total		
Second Week Total		
Third Week Total		
Fourth Week Total		
Total Earnings		

Test Your Skill

1. Add:

$2.49	$ 4.98	$8.95	$9.27	$ 4.56
3.65	14.20	2.62	0.03	14.86
1.50	10.04	3.56	1.45	5.98
2.10	0.37	7.85	5.06	0.27
				10.37

2. What expenses would you have if you cut lawns as a part-time job?_____

_____

3. Why is it necessary to keep a record of expenses and earnings?_____

_____

4. What is overtime pay? _____

5. Subtract:

$2.38	$49.50	$31.29	$45.61	$246.60	$341.59
−1.26	−2.39	−24.56	−9.98	−27.89	−92.68

6. Find the time:

   3:30 p.m. — 9:30 p.m._____h

   10:00 a.m. — 2:00 p.m._____h

   8:30 a.m. — 4:30 p.m._____h

   6:30 p.m. — 2:30 a.m._____h

   4:30 a.m. — 12:30 p.m._____h

   1:30 a.m. — 12:30 a.m._____h

7. From your experiences in the various shop areas, what part-time jobs could you work at?_____

_____

_____

8. Multiply:

$0.36	$1.76	$4.29	$36.50	$47.76	$38.79
×9	×8	×24	×6	×70	×35

9. Why is it to your advantage to find a part-time job?

_____

_____

_____

10. How do part-time jobs influence your final choice of employment?

_____

_____

_____

Topics and Activities for Class Discussion

1. Finding a part-time job will help you select a future career. Discuss.
2. Talk about what businesses in your area hire part-time student help.
3. Discuss the pros and cons of each student's part-time job.
4. What pay do you get for part-time jobs in your area? Discuss and compare.
5. If you are seeking a part-time job you should be aware of your appearance. Discuss.
6. What features does an employer look for in part-time help that he hires?
7. Visit the guidance office and encourage them to get in contact with businesses that hire part-time help, and to have job openings posted on the bulletin board.

CHAPTER SEVEN
WAGES

The Time Card

Study the sample time card below and answer the questions on the following page.

Employee Name				Payroll Number		
Social Ins. No.		Occupation		Hourly Rate of Pay		
Morning		Afternoon		Total Hours	Overtime		Total Hours
In	Out	In	Out		In	Out	
Signature		Total Hours Regular			Total Hours Overtime		

Deductions			Regular Pay		
Income Tax			Overtime Pay		
Unemployment Ins.			Total Pay		
Social Insurance			Total Deductions		
Total Deductions			Take-Home Pay		

1. Why is the hourly rate of pay included on the time card? _____

_____

2. Why is there a separate section on the time card for overtime?_____

_____

3. Why are total regular hours and total overtime hours calculated in separate columns?_____

_____

4. What is an employee number?_____

_____

5. Why is the signature of the employee included on the time card?_____

_____

6. What are deductions?_____

_____

7. What is Unemployment Insurance?_____

_____

8. What is take-home pay?_____

_____

9. What is total pay? _____

_____

Variety Store Worker

Joan has a job working for a variety store. She attends school, but she is allowed to work any time she is free from school. The following is a schedule for one of Joan's pay periods.

Monday	22	1:00 — 5:00
Tuesday	23	3:00 — 7:00
Wednesday	24	2:00 — 5:00
Thursday	25	3:00 — 5:00
Friday	26	2:00 — 4:00
Saturday	27	8:00 — 2:00

Joan works for $4.00 an hour. Fill in the time card below and calculate the hours and wages per day. Find the total for the pay period.

Day	Date	In	Out	Rate	Hours	Total	
					Total		

Deductions		
Income Tax	9	95
Unemployment Insurance	2	35
Total		

Earnings		
Total Earnings		
Total Deductions		
Take-Home Pay		

Hint: To find take-home pay, subtract total deductions from total earnings.

Figure the wages as outlined on the chart below.

In	Out	Hours	Hourly Rate	Total Wage	
8:00	12:00		$2.70		
9:00	3:00		$3.00		
10:00	5:00		$3.80		
12:00	6:00		$4.90		
3:00	6:00		$2.00		
11:00	5:00		$3.10		
3:00	5:00		$2.90		
10:00	4:00		$3.90		
9:00	4:00		$5.70		
8:00	3:00		$3.80		
8:00	5:00		$2.90		
9:00	5:00		$3.20		
12:00	5:00		$2.10		
1:00	6:00		$2.90		

1. Bill works from 8:00 a.m. to 4.30 p.m.

   (a) How many hours from 8:00 a.m. to 4:00 p.m.? _____

   (b) How many hours from 4:00 p.m. to 4:30 p.m.? _____

   (c) How many hours from 8:00 a.m. to 4:30 p.m.? _____

2. Fill in the hours worked:

In	Out	Hours	In	Out	Hours
8:30	10:30		10:30	4:30	
9:30	5:30		2:30	6:30	
9:30	2:30		10:30	5:30	
8:30	11:30		1:30	7:30	
1:30	6:30		2:30	8:30	
9:30	12:30		11:30	9:30	
10:30	8:30		12:30	3:30	
8:30	4:30		10:30	6:30	
12:30	6:30		1:30	5:30	
8:30	1:30		1:30	8:30	

3. Fill in the hours worked:

In	Out	Hours	In	Out	Hours
8:00	10:30		3:00	8:30	
9:00	12:30		11:00	4:30	
1:00	3:30		12:30	5:00	
2:00	6:30		9:00	2:30	
12:30	4:00		8:30	5:00	
2:30	7:00		3:30	9:00	
10:30	1:00		11:00	7:30	
9:30	3:00		1:00	5:30	
8:30	2:00		9:30	4:00	
10:00	3:30		8:00	4:30	

Caretaker's Helper

Robert works as a caretaker's helper in the local shopping centre. He keeps his own time sheet, and figures his wages at $3.50 an hour. He is paid every two weeks.

Find Robert's take-home pay for the two-week period.

First Week		Second Week	
Monday	3:30 — 5:00	Monday	3:30 — 6:00
Tuesday	3:30 — 6:00	Tuesday	4:00 — 5:30
Wednesday	4:00 — 5:30	Wednesday	3:30 — 5:30
Thursday	4:30 — 6:00	Thursday	4:30 — 6:00
Friday	3:30 — 6:30	Friday	4:00 — 6:00
Saturday	9:00 — 12:30	Saturday	12:00 — 5:00

First Week				Second Week			
Day	In	Out	Total Hours	Day	In	Out	Total Hours
Mon.				Mon.			
Tues.				Tues.			
Wed.				Wed.			
Thurs.				Thurs.			
Fri.				Fri.			
Sat.				Sat.			
Total Hours				Total Hours			

Deductions			Earnings		
Income Tax	28	55	Total Hours Week 1 and 2		
Unemployment Ins.	1	87	Total Pay		
Hospital Plan	2	10	Total Deductions		
Total Deductions			Take-Home Pay		

Punch Operator

Below is the time card for Linda Allan. She starts work at 8:00 a.m. Her lunch hour, for which she does not get paid, begins at 12:00 noon, and she completes work at 5:00 p.m. Fill out her time card for the five-day week.

Employee Name	Linda Allan		Payroll Number	8613	
Social Ins. No. 425-606-449		Occupation Punch Operator		Hourly Rate of Pay $6.40	

Morning		Afternoon		Total Hours	Overtime		Total Hours
In	Out	In	Out		In	Out	

Signature	Total Hours Regular			Total Hours Overtime	

Deductions			Regular Pay		
Income Tax	15	23	Overtime Pay		
Unemployment Ins.	1	73	Total Pay		
Social Insurance	2	78	Total Deductions		
Total Deductions			Take-Home Pay		

Clerk

Lloyd Taylor graduated from school and got a job as a clerk in a warehouse. He starts work at 8:30 and finishes at 5:30. He take his lunch hour, for which he is not paid, from 12:30 until 1:30. Fill out his time card.

Employee Name	Lloyd Taylor		Payroll Number		9245	
Social Ins. No. 783-603-448		Occupation Clerk		Hourly Rate of Pay		$ 3.80

Morning		Afternoon		Total Hours	Overtime		Total Hours
In	Out	In	Out		In	Out	

Signature	Total Hours Regular			Total Hours Overtime	

Deductions			Regular Pay		
Income Tax	12	28	Overtime Pay		
Unemployment Ins.	1	58	Total Pay		
Social Insurance	2	29	Total Deductions		
Total Deductions			Take-Home Pay		

Crane Operator

Jimmy Powers is a crane operator. His payroll number is 6758 and his Social Insurance number is 116-057-797. The regular rate of pay is $6.50 and his overtime rate is $8.50.

He worked Monday to Friday from 9:00 a.m. to 5:00 p.m. and had one hour for lunch for which he is not paid. On Monday, Wednesday and Friday he worked overtime from 6:00 p.m. to 9:00 p.m. His deductions were: income tax $19.38, Unemployment Insurance $1.98, Social Insurance $4.50.

Find Jimmy's take-home pay.

Employee Name				Payroll Number			
Social Ins. No.			Occupation		Hourly Rate of Pay		
Morning		Afternoon		Total Hours	Overtime		Total Hours
In	Out	In	Out		In	Out	
Signature		Total Hours Regular			Total Hours Overtime		

Deductions			Regular Pay		
Income Tax			Overtime Pay		
Unemployment Ins.			Total Pay		
Social Insurance			Total Deductions		
Total Deductions			Take-Home Pay		

Daily Pay Sheet

Some companies employ people to work for one day only. Below is a chart for one such company. All employees are allowed one hour for lunch, for which they are not paid. Find the take-home pay for each employee.

Hint: Subtract one hour for lunch.

Name	In	Out	Working Hours	Rate	Deduc-tions	Take-Home Pay	
Andy	9:00	4:00		2.10	1.03		
Chris	8:30	4:30		3.25	1.34		
Bradley	9:30	5:30		3.50	1.76		
Tracey	8:00	4:30		4.00	.97		
Kelly	8:30	5:00		3.20	1.24		
Mary	9:00	4:00		2.15	1.15		
Arnold	8:30	4:30		2.95	.92		
Vietta	9:00	5:30		3.10	1.07		
LeRoy	8.00	5:00		2.85	.87		
Allana	7:30	4:00		2.20	1.28		

Piece Work

Acme Tool Limited employs many graduates of Eastern Vocational School on a part-time basis. They are paid according to the number of articles they complete per day. For example:

Number of articles completed   50
Rate of pay per article completed . . . . $ 0.80
Total money earned (50 × $0.80) $40.00

Using the Tally Sheet below find the total earnings for each employee.

Name	Brian Allan	Sue Turner	Heather Jones
Article	Scraper	Circuit Dial	Switches
Rate per article	$0.60	$0.65	$0.75
Number of pieces completed per day			
Monday	40	27	28
Tuesday	38	33	34
Wednesday	46	29	36
Thursday	44	32	32
Friday	41	30	33
Total pieces completed			
Wages			

Payroll for Ace Towing Company

The Ace Towing Company operates a small establishment and has six employees. From the information provided fill out the Calculation of Earnings Form, and issue a weekly pay cheque for each employee.

| Fred Hewitt | President | Rate of Pay: | $9.00/h |

Mon. — 8 h	Thur. — 10 h
Tues. — 8 h	Fri. — 9 h
Wed. — 10 h	Sat. — 10 h

| Susan Ogden | Secretary | Rate of Pay: | $4.25/h |

Mon. — 8 h	Thur. — 8 h
Tues. — 8 h	Fri. — 8 h
Wed. — 8 h	Sat. — 4 h

| Bill Perth | Maintenance | Rate of Pay: | $3.90/h |

Mon. — no work	Thur. — 8 h
Tues. — 8 h	Fri. — 8 h
Wed. — 9 h	Sat. — 10 h

| John Rose | Driver | Rate of Pay: | $4.60/h |

Mon. — 10 h	Thur. — 5 h
Tues. — 12 h	Fri. — 8 h
Wed. — 6 h	Sat. — 7 h

| Diane Burke | Driver | Rate of Pay: | $4.65/h |

Mon. — 8 h	Thur. — 7 h
Tues. — 10 h	Fri. — 5 h
Wed. — 8 h	Sat. — 8 h

| Bruce Carson | Driver | Rate of Pay: | $4.75/h |

Mon. — 6 h	Thur. — 7 h
Tues. — 10 h	Fri. — 10 h
Wed. — 8 h	Sat. — 6 h

Name and Occupation	Working Days						Total Hours	Rate	Gross Pay	Deductions			Take-Home Pay
	M	T	W	T	F	S				Fed. Tax	U.I.	Hosp. Plan	
Fred Hewitt										42.52	1.59	1.64	
Susan Ogden										19.36	1.48	1.09	
Bill Perth										24.17	1.51	1.40	
John Rose										21.34	1.49	1.30	
Peter Brown										26.34	1.56	1.49	
Diane Burke										25.98	1.53	1.41	

Earnings Statement

Earnings | Deductions | Net Pay

Salary | Overtime | Total | Pension | Income Tax | Hospital Plan | Medical Plan | Group Insurance | Savings Bonds | Unemployment Insurance | Misc.

Name

Occupation

Employment No.

Ace Towing Co.

ACE TOWING CO.

Pay to the Order of

Date

$

Dollars

Cheque No. **101**

Earnings Statement

Earnings | Deductions | Net Pay

Salary | Overtime | Total | Pension | Income Tax | Hospital Plan | Medical Plan | Group Insurance | Savings Bonds | Unemployment Insurance | Misc.

Name

Occupation

Employment No.

Ace Towing Co.

ACE TOWING CO.

Pay to the Order of

Date

$

Dollars

Cheque No. **102**

Earnings Statement

Earnings			Deductions								Net Pay
Salary	Overtime	Total	Pension	Income Tax	Hospital Plan	Medical Plan	Group Insurance	Savings Bonds	Unemployment Insurance	Misc.	

Name

Occupation

Employment No.

Ace Towing Co.

ACE TOWING CO.

Date

Pay to the Order of

$ _____ Dollars

Cheque No. __103__

Earnings Statement

Earnings			Deductions								Net Pay
Salary	Overtime	Total	Pension	Income Tax	Hospital Plan	Medical Plan	Group Insurance	Savings Bonds	Unemployment Insurance	Misc.	

Name

Occupation

Employment No.

Ace Towing Co.

ACE TOWING CO.

Date

Pay to the Order of

$ _____ Dollars

Cheque No. __104__

Earnings Statement

			Deductions							Net Pay
	Pension	Income Tax	Hospital Plan	Medical Plan	Group Insurance	Savings Bonds	Unemployment Insurance	Misc.		

Earnings

Salary	Occupation	Overtime	Employment Number	Total	Name

Ace Towing Co.

ACE TOWING CO.

Date _____

Pay to the Order of _____

$ _____

_____ Dollars

Cheque No. ___ **105**

Earnings Statement

			Deductions							Net Pay
	Pension	Income Tax	Hospital Plan	Medical Plan	Group Insurance	Savings Bonds	Unemployment Insurance	Misc.		

Earnings

Salary	Occupation	Overtime	Employment Number	Total	Name

Ace Towing Co.

ACE TOWING CO.

Date _____

Pay to the Order of _____

$ _____

_____ Dollars

Cheque No. ___ **106**

Test Your Skill

1. Find the hours between:

   8:00—12:00_____ h   8:00—4:30_____ h

   6:00—10:00_____ h   7:30—2:00_____ h

   1:30— 3:30_____ h   6:30—9:30_____ h

2. Multiply:

$1.40	$1.90	$1.25	$1.80	$3.90	$2.45
× 40	× 46	× 16	× 25	× 36	× 27

3. What is gross pay? _____

4. What are deductions?_____

5. What is take-home pay?_____

6. Subtract:

$21.36	$48.83	$ 9.58	$14.59	$38.41	$22.80
−3.95	−6.24	− 0.78	−2.90	−7.58	−4.97

7. Find Arnold's take-home pay if he works 23 hours at $4.50 and his total deductions are $16.39.

_____

8. Add:

$ 3.26	$ 3.01	$ 5.46	$26.59	$86.30	$ 3.95
0.47	1.43	2.06	3.58	21.52	0.27
1.26	0.79	0.78	0.47	16.30	21.36
			20.46	14.29	2.50
					0.27

9. Peter works from 9:00 a.m. to 3:00 p.m. five days a week. His hourly rate of pay is $4.40. Total deductions are $12.48.

   (a) How many hours does he work a week?_____

   (b) What is his rate of pay?_____

(c) How much is Peter's gross pay? _____

(d) What are his total deductions? _____

(e) How much is his take-home pay? _____

10. Why is it necessary for a company to have a time card?

_____

_____

_____

11. Why should you check your pay envelope carefully before leaving your place of employment?

_____

_____

_____

12. Why is speed and accuracy when you work important to both your employer and yourself?

_____

_____

_____

_____

Topics and Activities for Class Discussion

1. When seeking a full-time job you should consider more than just pay. Discuss.
2. What questions should you ask your prospective employer before you agree to work for him?
3. How can you prepare yourself for filling out a job application?
4. Discuss with your class how you should appear when you seek employment.
5. What do you owe the company you work for? Discuss.
6. Does your school help you seek employment at the end of your formal education? Discuss what your school can do to help you find employment.
7. Visit some employment possibilities in your area.
8. Set up practice interviews in your class.

CHAPTER EIGHT
BUDGETS

Income, Expenses and Savings

Making a list of income (what you earn) and expenses (what you spend) helps you understand how you spend your money and helps you save money.

Find the total expenses for each person and calculate their savings:

Bob Becker	Total
Income	$5.00
Expenses . . . . $ 1.00 0.25 1.00 0.50 0.25	
Savings	

Mark Holmes	Total
Income	$7.00
Expenses . . . . $ 0.25 0.10 1.00 0.30 2.00 0.10 0.15	
Savings	

Susan Carlaw	Total
Income	$6.50
Expenses . . . . $ 0.15 1.05 0.30 0.10 0.90 1.00	
Savings	

Bradley Smith	Total
Income	$10.50
Expenses . . . . $ 2.00 0.15 0.25 0.80 0.25 0.10 1.10 2.40	
Savings	

Monthly Budget Planning

1. John found that his weekly allowance was not enough to buy the things he needed. Rather than ask his parents for more money, he found that he could earn his own money by doing odd jobs for his neighbours.

Income			Expenses		
Oct.	2 — Allowance	$2.50	Oct.	5 — Suit cleaned	$3.50
	3 — Grass cutting	3.00		9 — Entertainment	2.20
	7 — Wash windows	3.00		15 — New pen	0.69
	9 — Allowance	2.50		19 — New socks	1.80
	10 — Car wash	1.50		23 — Gift	3.25
	14 — Cut grass	3.00		29 — Entertainment	3.50
	16 — Allowance	2.50		30 — Bathing suit	6.50
	17 — Clean basement	4.00			
	20 — Trim hedge	1.25			
	23 — Allowance	2.50			
	25 — Rake leaves	1.50			
	26 — Deliver papers	6.60			

Complete John's budget sheet:

Date	Income	Total	Date	Expense	Total
	Total			**Total**	

How much money did John save for the month of October? _____

216

2. Susan did babysitting to help increase her income. She received an allowance of $2.50 a week, and took as many jobs as possible during the week. To keep track of her income and expenses she kept a budget sheet.

Income

April 2 —	Allowance	$2.50
9 —	Babysitting	5.50
9 —	Allowance	2.50
12 —	Babysitting	4.00
16 —	Allowance	2.50
17 —	Babysitting	3.00
19 —	Babysitting	3.75
21 —	Babysitting	4.50
23 —	Allowance	2.50
25 —	Babysitting	6.50
30 —	Allowance	7.50
31 —	Babysitting	7.00

Expenses

April 3 —	Lipstick	$1.79
5 —	Nylons	2.00
13 —	Gift	4.50
17 —	Blouse	6.95
25 —	Pen	0.99
27 —	Sandals	6.98
29 —	Book	2.50
30 —	Record	4.50

Date		Income	Total	Date		Expense	Total
		Total				Total	

How much did Susan save during the month of April? _____

3. Joe increased his income during the winter by doing winter jobs. He received his weekly allowance of $3.50, but since he was working he was expected to pay for most of his own expenses. Calculate his budget for January.

Income

Jan. 1 — Allowance.............$3.50
     5 — Snow shovelling...... 3.00
     6 — Snow shovelling...... 3.00
     8 — Allowance.......... 3.50
    12 — Clean basement...... 1.50
    15 — Allowance.......... 3.50
    16 — Snow shovelling...... 2.50
    17 — Snow shovelling...... 4.00
    23 — Allowance.......... 3.50
    26 — Deliver handbills..... 4.00
    30 — Allowance.......... 3.50
    30 — Pushing cars......... 2.00

Expenses

Jan. 1 — Record.............$4.95
     7 — Gift............... 3.50
     9 — Tie................ 4.50
    20 — Gym shoes......... 6.95
    21 — Entertainment....... 4.00
    23 — Book.............. 2.75
    24 — Model kit.......... 2.95

Date		Income	Total	Date		Expense	Total
		Total				**Total**	

How much did he save during the month of January?_____

4. Calculate Mary's budget for the month of March.

Income		Expenses	
Mar. 3—Allowance	$3.25	Mar. 4 — Lipstick	$1.75
5—Babysitting	2.75	6 — Deodorant	1.59
7—Mother's helper	4.35	9 — Nylons	1.95
10—Allowance	3.25	15 — Record	4.80
14—Babysitting	4.50	17 — Hair spray	1.99
17—Allowance	3.25	21 — Pen	0.79
20—Sold books	7.00	26 — Nylons	1.95
24—Allowance	3.25	27 — Cologne	3.98
25—Birthday gift	5.00	30 — Entertainment	5.75
28—Babysitting	3.50		
31—Allowance	3.25		
31—Babysitting	7.50		

Date		Income	Total	Date		Expense	Total
		Total				**Total**	

How much did Mary save during the month of March? _____

219

Yearly Budget Planning

Calculate the Jones's budget for the year. The total of their expenses plus their savings must equal the income per month.

Month	Monthly Income	Expenses				Savings
		House	Car	Food	Misc.	
Jan.	$ 950.00		$ 60.00	$198.00	$150.00	$200.00
Feb.	950.00	$229.00	72.00		160.00	170.00
March	950.00	215.00		189.00	200.00	150.00
April	950.00	236.00	66.00	194.00		190.00
May	1010.00	218.00	173.00	207.00	227.00	
June	1010.00		169.00	186.00	198.00	135.00
July	1010.00	230.00	84.00		184.00	141.00
Aug.	1010.00	240.00	96.00	203.00	146.00	
Sept.	1090.00	229.00	157.00	209.00		135.00
Oct.	1090.00		66.00	205.00	163.00	206.00
Nov.	1090.00	229.00		210.00	153.00	264.00
Dec.	1090.00	238.00	62.00	208.00	189.00	
					Total	

1. List eight jobs that you could do to help increase your income.

   (a)_____ (e)_____

   (b)_____ (f)_____

   (c)_____ (g)_____

   (d)_____ (h)_____

2. Why should you make a list of your income? _____

   _____

3. Why should you list your expenses? _____

   _____

4. How does a budget sheet help you keep track of your income and expenses? _____

   _____

5. Why should you make more than you spend?_____

   _____

6. What should you do with the money that is not spent?_____

   _____

7. Why should you try to save some money each month?_____

   _____

8. Why would a family keep a yearly budget?_____

   _____

9. What is meant by "misc. expenses"?_____

   _____

10. Why would your income change during the year?_____

   _____

Home Budgeting

Chris helped her mother at home by keeping track of household expenses and operating costs. She divided the expenses into:

1. Services, such as telephone, heat, public utilities, mortgage, insurance and service calls.

2. Operating expenses, such as food and non-food products that were used to keep the home operating properly.

Below is a list of the expenses for the month of March. Fill in the chart and find the total.

March 1 — Mortgage............$310.00   March 16 — Service (drain)..$28.60
        4 — Insurance............ 14.00   20 — Food.......... 47.30
        6 — Food................ 33.85   21 — Heat........... 68.50
        7 — Service (dryer repairs).. 16.75   22 — Food.......... 14.50
        9 — Food................ 19.45   25 — Service (washer) 7.00
     10 — Telephone............ 9.00   26 — Milk........... 2.53
     12 — Food................ 56.65   27 — Food.......... 11.90
     13 — Public utilities........ 28.62   28 — Food.......... 27.40
     14 — Food................ 39.76

Date	Services	Cost	Date	Operating Expenses	Cost
	Total			Total	

Find the total expenses for the month of March. _____

Find the amount of money needed each week to operate the house. (Hint: Divide by 4.)_____

222

Below is Chris's list of expenses for the month of April. Fill in the chart and find the total.

April 1 — Mortgage . . . . $310.00   April 17 — Heat $46.57

       3 — Food . . . . 26.25   19 — Food 37.95

       5 — Insurance . . . . 14.00   21 — Food 46.15

       8 — Service (T.V.) . . . . 6.50   23 — Service (stove) 15.40

     10 — Food . . . . 43.15   24 — Food 3.90

     11 — Telephone . . . . 9.70   27 — Food 7.50

     13 — Food . . . . 28.75   29 — Service (furnace) . . . 15.00

     15 — Public utilities . . . . 37.50   30 — Food 36.15

Date		Services	Cost		Date		Operating Expenses	Cost	
		Total					**Total**		

Find the total expenses for the month of April. _____

Find the amount of money needed each week to operate the house. _____

Below is the list of expenses for the month of May. Fill in the chart and find the total.

May	1 — Mortgage........$310.00	May 17 — Food.............$29.82
	2 — Food............. 26.25	20 — Public utilities...... 34.56
	4 — Food............. 86.52	21 — Food............. 16.45
	6 — Insurance........ 14.00	24 — Service (T.V.)...... 25.25
	7 — Food............. 36.73	25 — Food............. 43.82
	11 — Food............. 20.54	27 — Heat............. 53.63
	14 — Telephone........ 9.73	28 — Food............. 14.57
	16 — Service	30 — Service (T.V.)...... 7.50
	(water heater).. 12.50	

Date	Services	Cost		Date	Operating Expenses	Cost	
Total				**Total**			

Find the total expenses for the month of May. _____

Find the amount of money needed each week to operate the house. _____

Total for the month of March		
Total for the month of April		
Total for the month of May		
Total for the three months		

What is the average cost of operating the home for one month? (Divide by 3.) _____

Buying a Car

Bill learned to service a car in the Auto Shop at York Vocational School. He liked working with cars so he decided to buy one. Bill found this advertisement in the Cars For Sale column in the paper.

> 6-year-old Chevrolet, Red and blue — good condition — whitewalls, radio, factory air-conditioned — Automatic
> Call 444-1621

Bill went to see the car. What points should he consider before buying the car?

1._____ 4._____

2._____ 5._____

3._____ 6._____

Bill wanted to calculate the price of the car.

Advertised price of the car	$1495.00
Sales tax	$104.30
Purchase price of the car	

Bill paid a down payment of $350.00 and financed the amount still owing over twelve months at a total finance charge of $240.05.

Finding the Amount to be Financed	
Purchase price of the car	
Less the down payment	
Amount to be financed	

Finding the Monthly Payment	
Amount to be financed	
Add finance charge	
Total to be financed	
Monthly payment (divide the total to be financed by 12)	

Bill had to buy a driver's permit for $12.00 and ownership and licence plates which cost $40.00. He also had to buy insurance for his car and the agent told him that it would cost $385.00 for one year's coverage.

Extra Costs	
Driver's permit	
Ownership and licence	
Insurance	
Total	

Bill wanted to calculate the actual cost of the car and extras before he could drive it.

Cost of Car and Extras	
Advertised price of the car	
Sales tax	
Finance charges	
Driver's permit	
Ownership and licence	
Insurance	
Total	

Operating a Car

Bill was proud of his car, and kept it clean and in good operating condition. He was concerned about the kilometrage he was getting with each litre of gas. He decided to check the kilometrage before each filling and keep a record of the number of litres of gas. In this way, he could find how many kilometres he drove and the number of litres it took to fill the tank. First he had to learn how to subtract the first reading from the second reading.

Practise finding the distance travelled from the following readings:

First Reading	Second Reading	Kilometrage
1 465	1 565	
23 265	23 415	
36 045	36 385	
42 560	42 790	
76 453	76 539	
32 653	32 887	
5 689	6 312	
45 896	47 853	
58 149	61 205	
5 196	7 236	
9 186	10 687	
10 694	14 720	

Bill found that dividing the number of litres used into the number of kilometres travelled would tell him how many kilometres his car went on each litre of gas.

$$\text{no. of litres } \overline{)\text{number of kilometres travelled}}$$

Calculate the km/L in the following:

Kilometres Travelled	Litres of Gas Used	km/L
165	5	
228	8	
297	9	
124	4	
178	6	
145	5	

Fill in the missing parts to complete the chart:

Kilometres Travelled	Litres of Gas Used	km/L
	6	27
248		31
180	10	
	9	29
276		23

228

Using the price list below, find Bill's car operating expenses for one month.

Gas	30.9¢/L
Oil	$1.40/L
Lubrication	$4.50
Filter	$6.75
Tire Rotation	$8.50

March   3—gasoline—10 L

            7—oil change—5 L

            7—oil filter

         10—tire rotation

         18—gasoline—25 L

         23—flat tire repair $6.00

         25—gasoline—12 L

         26—repairs—parts cost $8.45

         29—gasoline—15 L

         29—lubrication

Date		Operating Expenses	Cost	
		Total Car Operating Expenses		

Test Your Skill

1.

$110.00	$ 4.39	$ 42.83	$ 49.00	$ 24.04
23.94	5.00	0.72	28.53	3.36
4.36	6.23	50.03	4.23	154.20
9.27	14.38	4.93	110.00	3.93

2. What is a mortgage?_____

3. Why is it important to pay your bills on time?_____

_____

4. What is a budget?_____

5. Why is it wise to have more money available than you think you will spend?_____

_____

6. Why should you keep track of your home expenses?_____

_____

7. Divide: 4)$26.38   5)$243.95   7)$863.45

3)$46.26   6)$4.56   8)$936.56

8. What is Sales Tax?_____

9. Who receives the money from a Sales Tax?_____

10. What is interest? _____

11. Why must you pay interest when you borrow money?_____

_____

12. What permits must you secure before you may drive your car?_____

13. Why is the cost of a car before you can drive it more than the advertised price?_____
_____

14.
9 876	6 843	3 624	42 361	6 040	7 685
− 3 294	− 294	− 1 409	− 9 493	− 2 178	− 2 198

15. 23$\overline{)1127}$ 93$\overline{)36\ 454}$

    7$\overline{)59\ 434}$ 9$\overline{)57\ 322}$

16. Why should you keep a monthly budget?_____
_____
_____

17. What facts should be considered when you purchase a used car?_____
_____
_____

Topics and Activities for Class Discussion

1. Why is it important to save money?
2. Discuss ways of keeping your bills paid on time.
3. Why is keeping your credit record important to you? What happens if you develop a bad credit record?
4. Arrange a class visit to a used car dealer. Learn about prices, cars available, financing, guarantees and what features to look at when buying a used car.
5. Keep a record of all income and expenses you have over a month. Discuss the results with your class.
6. Check the ads in your local newspaper to learn where to get good service for your car. Compare prices and reliability. Visit a service station and see what care they take with cars they are repairing. Discuss in class your findings.
7. Take a survey of gasoline prices in your area. Discuss prices in class.
8. If you use self-serve gasoline stations, discuss the advantages and disadvantages.
9. Suppose that you wish to start living on your own. Discuss your budgeting needs.

CHAPTER NINE
OPERATING A HOME

In an Apartment

Pete decided to lease his own apartment after he graduated from Southern Vocational School. Once he decided which apartment he wanted to rent, he received a lease from the landlord. The lessor explained that Pete must pay a rent of $315.00 a month at the beginning of each month for a duration of one year. Pete read the lease carefully to make sure he understood all the terms. Then he signed the lessee section of the contract and had a friend witness his signature.

1. Explain the following words.

   lease_____

   apartment_____

   rent_____

   landlord_____

   lessor_____

   duration_____

   terms_____

   contract_____

   lessee_____

   witness_____

2. Why must Pete pay his rent on time?_____

   _____

3. Why must Pete pay one month's rent in advance?_____

   _____

4. Why is it important to read the contents of the lease?_____

   _____

5. What happens if Pete breaks the terms of the lease?_____

   _____

6. How can Pete legally break his lease?_____

   _____

7. List five ways in which Pete can be a good apartment dweller.

_____

_____

_____

_____

_____

8. At a rent of $215.00 per month, what is the rent for one year?

_____

9. Bill makes $640.00 a month. How much did he have left after paying $229.50 rent?

_____

10. One month Howard paid $237.00 rent, $13.60 for the telephone and $18.90 for electric power. What was his total expense for the month?

_____

11. John makes $180.00 a week as a part-time assistant mechanic. How much must he save each week for rent if he pays $243.00 per month?

_____

12. Operating expenses for one month cost Sam $209.00 rent, $23.66 for electricity and $12.50 for the telephone. What are his total operating expenses for the month?

_____

13. On a weekly salary of $165.00 per week, how much money is left at the end of a month after paying $209.00 rent, $18.30 for electricity, and $12.29 for the telephone? (4 pay periods per month)

_____

Rick earns a monthly salary of $980.00. He has made himself a monthly budget accounting for his complete salary of $980.00. Fill the blanks in his budget with the suitable answer and find the totals.

Month	Rent	Trans-portation	Enter-tainment	Operating Expenses	Clothing	Savings
Jan.	$210.00	$ 90.00	$ 63.00	$180.00	$223.00	$214.00
Feb.	210.00	147.00	Took a vacation 311.00	197.00	55.00	60.00
Mar.	210.00	153.00	127.00	148.00		236.00
Apr.	210.00		180.00	183.00	27.00	197.00
May	210.00	146.50	126.75		187.95	131.00
June	210.00	Motorcycle repairs	97.40	212.80	78.56	100.00
July	210.00	168.00	139.00	236.50	39.65	
Aug.	210.00	98.62	126.90		114.70	174.48
Sept.	210.00	87.93	Vacation 295.75		37.90	150.00
Oct.	210.00	151.90		203.65	38.56	226.00
Nov.	210.00	165.25	76.30	207.67	Winter coat	124.00
Dec.	210.00	Vehicle insurance 225.00	97.65	130.00	New suit 231.50	

| Total for the year | | | | | | |

1. In which month did Rick save the most money?_____

2. Why are transportation costs higher in some months than in others?_____

_____

3. When were Rick's operating expenses the highest?_____

4. During what month did he spend most on clothing?_____

5. Why should he save money every month if possible?_____

_____

_____

6. Why is it a good idea to keep a budget of your expenses and income?_____

_____

_____

_____

7. How could Rick's wife help him save more money?_____

_____

_____

_____

8. Use each word once to fill the blanks.

one	budgeting	lease	lessor
$210.00	spend	contract	
budget	month	income	
notice	lessee	landlord	

Rick pays _____ rent for his apartment. He signed a _____ and must pay his rent at the

beginning of each _____. A _____ helps him keep his expenses below his _____, so

that he does not _____ too much. Because of wise _____ he has been able

to save money during the year. Before Rick can break his _____ with the _____ of the

apartment he must give his _____ in writing _____ month in advance so that the

_____ will be able to rent to a new _____.

In a Condominium

Pete's savings after several years were enough for him to consider buying a condominium. He went to a real estate agent and was shown some condominiums that were for sale. He selected one with a reasonable down payment and which carried for $396.00 a month. The carrying charges included the principal, interest and taxes. The down payment was $6,000.00, which left a mortgage of $36,000.00. Pete visited a lawyer to have him check the deed and make sure it was a safe and wise investment.

1. Explain the following words.

   real estate_____

   agent_____

   down payment_____

   principal_____

   interest_____

   taxes_____

   mortgage_____

   lawyer_____

   deed_____

   investment_____

2. Why did Pete decide to buy a home instead of renting?

   _____

   _____

3. Why did he go to a real estate agent?

   _____

   _____

4. Why was it important for him to visit a lawyer before he signed any papers?

   _____

   _____

   _____

   _____

5. Why must Pete pay his mortgage on time?_____

_____

6. What expenses would Pete have in owning a condominium that he would not have in renting an apartment?

_____

_____

_____

_____

7. What features of a condominium should be considered before purchasing it? _____

_____

_____

_____

_____

_____

8. Pete paid $6,000.00 down payment, which left a mortgage of $36,000.00. What was the selling price of the house?

_____

9. Find Pete's total expenses if moving cost $235.00, the lawyer's fee was $267.00 and miscellaneous expenses were $130.00.

_____

10. Before moving into his new home, Pete bought a stove for $563.50, a used refrigerator for $350.00, and a washer for $245.00. How much did Pete spend for new equipment?

_____

11. There was a $20.00 fee to connect the electric power, and $15.00 to connect the telephone. What did it cost Pete to have these services connected to his home?

_____

12. At a sale Pete found a $164.00 lawn mower for $\frac{1}{4}$ off and a set of garden tools at $34.50 for $\frac{1}{3}$ off. How much did he pay for the equipment?

_____

13. Curtains for the bedroom cost $69.00, for the living room $89.60 and for the kitchen $12.95. What was the total cost for curtains?

_____

14. With the information from above, complete the chart:

Equipment and furnishings			Services		
Stove			Telephone		
Refrigerator			Electric power		
Washer			Lawyer		
Lawn mower			Down payment		
Curtains			Moving expenses		
Garden tools			Miscellaneous		
Total			Total		

Fill in the chart below to find Pete's expenses for one year.

Month	Telephone	Electric power (two months)	Heat	Mortgage	Miscellaneous Expenses	
Jan.	$ 9.80	$33.74	$87.50	$394.20	Insurance	$132.40
Feb.	16.50	—	73.40	394.20	Tile	78.90
Mar.	12.40	49.67	62.50	394.20	Paint	54.50
Apr.	9.80	—	53.50	394.20	Storm Door	79.95
May	23.50	43.50	37.40	394.20	Plants	15.50
June	23.90	—	—	394.20	Lawn Furniture	23.50
July	9.80	35.75	—	394.20	Insurance	132.40
Aug.	9.80	—	—	394.20	New Patio	248.50
Sept.	12.45	28.67	—	394.20	Paint	30.20
Oct.	15.20	—	47.80	394.20	Rug	79.75
Nov.	16.35	38.67	59.80	394.20	Paint	23.50
Dec.	17.27	—	72.40	394.20	Chair	169.40
Total						

1. What is the average cost per month for the telephone?

2. What is the average two-months cost for electric power?

3. What is the average cost of heat per month?

Find Pete's monthly operating expenses and complete the chart below.

Month	Total Expenses
January	
February	
March	
April	
May	
June	
July	
August	
September	
October	
November	
December	
Yearly Total	

Find his average monthly expense.

Topics and Activities for Class Discussion

1. Look at the ads in your local newspaper for apartments for rent. Compare prices and features. Discuss your research in class.
2. Ask for a sample lease for an apartment that is being rented. Read and discuss in class.
3. Discuss ways that you can be a good tenant.
4. Discuss why it may be to your advantage to live at home until you have saved some money.
5. Take a class trip to an area that is selling new homes. Talk to the salespeople and learn about models of homes available, quality of construction, financing arrangements and whether you qualify as a purchaser. Discuss your observations in class.
6. Make a bulletin board display of homes for sale.
7. Visit your guidance department. See if they can help you find a place to live if you need help. Encourage your guidance department to help you.
8. Make a bulletin board display of apartments to rent, rooms to rent, flats for rent and other suitable places to live.

CHAPTER TEN
GRAPHS

Bar Graphs

Bar graphs are used to convey statistical information quickly in an easy-to-read manner.

Study the graph below.

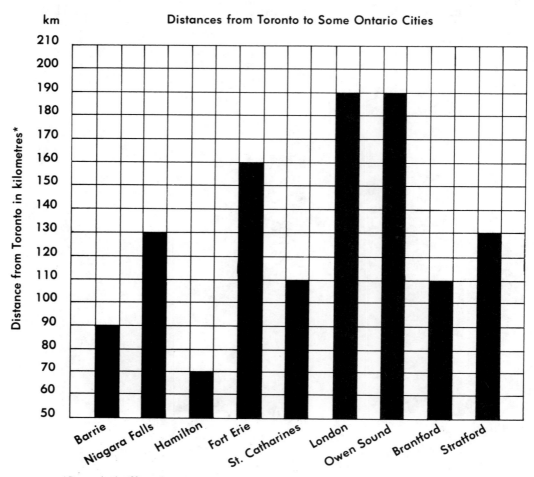

Distances from Toronto to Some Ontario Cities

km

*Rounded off to the nearest ten.

Parts of a bar graph:

1. *Title*—at the top of the graph
2. *Scale*—at the left side of the graph
3. *Guide line*—at the bottom of the graph
4. *Data*—on the guide line

After studying the graph above, answer these questions:

1. What is the title of the graph?

2. Why is the scale in 10's of km?

3. To how many cities is the distance from Toronto shown on the graph?

4. How many km is it from Toronto to:

(a) Barrie?   (d) Fort Erie?   (g) Owen Sound?

(b) Niagara Falls?   (e) St. Catharines?   (h) Brantford?

(c) Hamilton?   (f) London?   (i) Stratford?

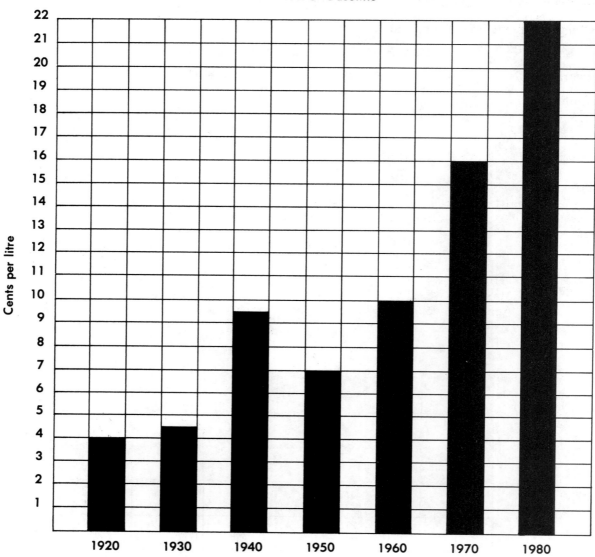

Cost of Gasoline

1. What is the title of the graph? _____

2. What is the scale of the graph? _____

3. What information is given on the guide line? _____

4. How much was gas per litre in:

      (a)   1980? _____   (e)   1970? _____

      (b)   1920? _____   (f)   1930? _____

      (c)   1960? _____   (g)   1950? _____

      (d)   1940? _____

5. How much more was gas in 1970 than in 1920? _____

6. How much less was gas in 1950 than in 1980? _____

7. How much more was gas in 1960 than in 1930? _____

Create bar graphs to show the following data:

1. Title: car sales for one year
2. Scale: by thousands of cars
3. Guide line: by each month from January to December
4. Data:

Jan.	3 500	May	10 000	Sept.	1 000
Feb.	4 000	June	5 000	Oct.	8 000
Mar.	2 500	July	2 000	Nov.	1 500
April	5 000	Aug.	6 000	Dec.	3 000

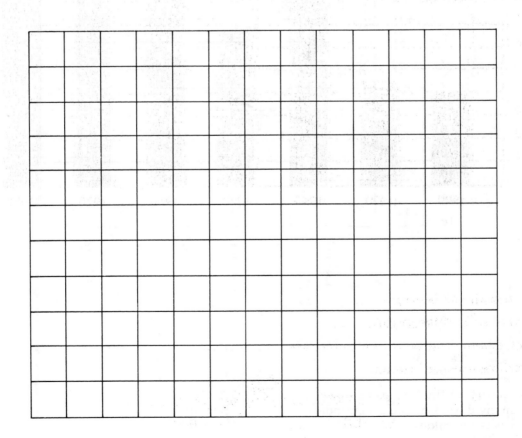

Line Graphs

The line graph is used to show comparisons and changes between pieces of information.

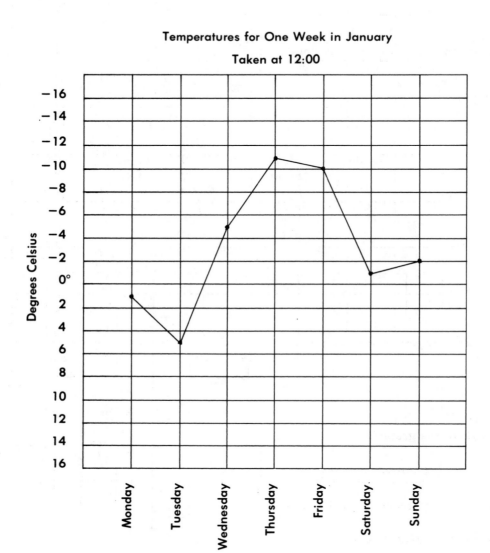

Temperatures for One Week in January

Taken at 12:00

1. What is the title of the line graph above?
2. For how many days does the graph indicate the temperature?
3. What day was the coldest?
4. What day was the warmest?
5. Why is the dot sometimes halfway between the lines?
6. What was the temperature on Monday? Tuesday? Wednesday? Thursday? Friday? Saturday? Sunday?

School Ticket Sales

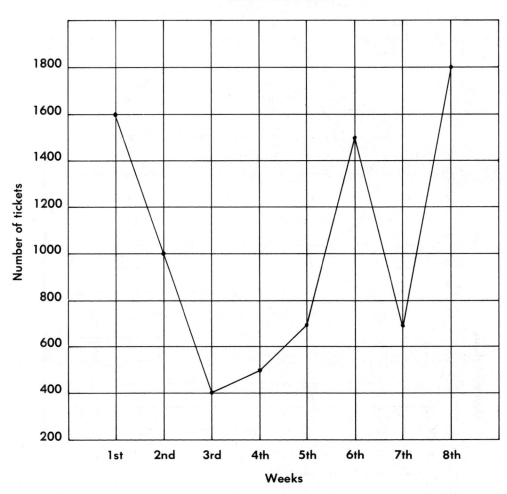

1. What is the title of the graph? _____

2. What information is given on the scale? _____

3. What information is given on the guide line? _____

4. Which week had the greatest sales? _____

5. Which week had the least sales? _____

6. How many tickets were sold in week 4? _____

7. How many tickets were sold in week 7? _____

8. How many more tickets were sold in week 1 than in week 7? _____

9. How many more tickets were sold in week 8 than in week 2? _____

249

Create line graphs to show the following statistical information.

1. Title: accumulated kilometres per year
2. Scale: by thousands of kilometres
3. Guide line: by years as below
4. Data:

(year)	1970	15 000	1975	7 000
	1971	8 000	1976	11 000
	1972	2 000	1977	2 000
	1973	6 000	1978	3 000
	1974	9 000	1979	1 000

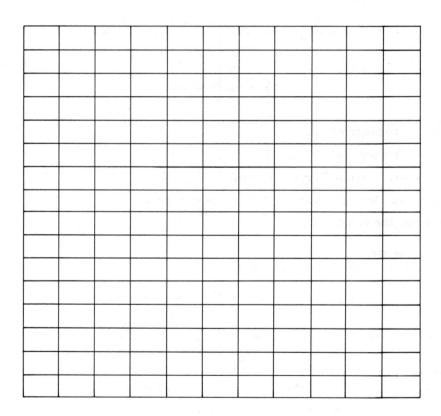

Circle Graphs

The circle graph shows the relation of one part to another and of one part to the whole.

Study the graph below.

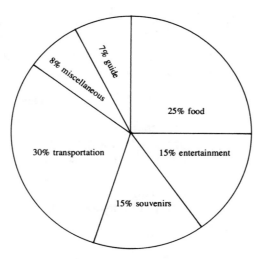

Expenses for a Trip

1. What item was most expensive? _____
2. What item was least expensive? _____
3. Which cost more, miscellaneous items or guides? _____
4. By what percentage did transportation cost more than food? _____
5. Which two items cost the same? _____

Study the circle graph below.

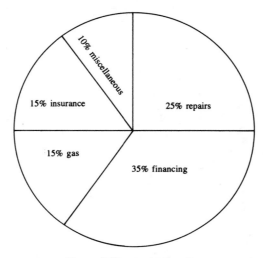

Cost of Operating a Car

1. Which item cost the most? _____
2. Which item cost the least? _____
3. How much more was insurance than gas? _____
4. How much more was gas than miscellaneous? _____

On the circle graph below record the following information.

Title: school sports equipment

25% football
30% track and field
20% baseball
10% volleyball
10% badminton
 5% field hockey

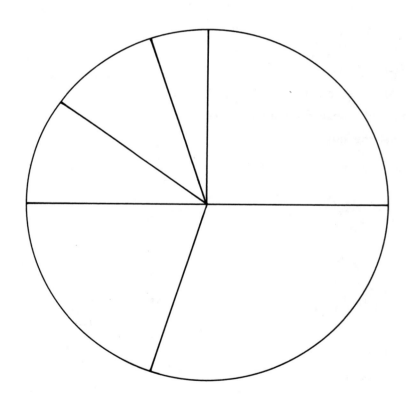